Instructor's Guide for College Physics

Eugenia Etkina
Rutgers University

David Brookes
Florida International University

Alan Van Heuvelen
Rutgers University

PEARSON

Boston Columbus Indianapolis New York San Francisco Upper Saddle River
Amsterdam Cape Town Dubai London Madrid Milan Munich Paris Montréal Toronto
Delhi Mexico City São Paulo Sydney Hong Kong Seoul Singapore Taipei Tokyo

Publisher: Jim Smith
Project Managers: Katie Conley and Beth Collins
Managing Development Editor: Cathy Murphy
Assistant Editor: Kyle Doctor
Team Lead, Program and Project Management, Physical Sciences: Corinne Benson
Director of Production: Erin Gregg
Full-Service Production and Composition: PreMedia Global, Inc.
Illustrator: PreMedia Global, Inc.
Manufacturing Buyer: Jeff Sargent
Marketing Manager: Will Moore
Cover Designer: Riezebos-Holzbaur Design Group and Seventeenth Street Studios
Cover Photo Credit: © Markus Altmann/Corbis

1 2 3 4 5 6 7 8 9 10—DOH—17 16 15 14 13

www.pearsonhighered.com

ISBN 10: 0-321-86363-1
ISBN 13: 978-0-321-86363-8

Contents

	Introduction	1
1	Kinematics: Motion in One Dimension	9
2	Newtonian Mechanics	15
3	Applying Newton's Laws	23
4	Circular Motion	29
5	Impulse and Linear Momentum	35
6	Work and Energy	41
7	Extended Bodies at Rest	50
8	Rotational Motion	56
9	Gases	62
10	Static Fluids	69
11	Fluids in Motion	74
12	First Law of Thermodynamics	79
13	Second Law of Thermodynamics	85
14	Electric Charge, Force, and Energy	89
15	The Electric Field	95
16	DC Circuits	101
17	Magnetism	107

18 Electromagnetic Induction 114
19 Vibrational Motion 120
20 Mechanical Waves 126
21 Reflection and Refraction 133
22 Mirrors and Lenses 138
23 Wave Optics 144
24 Electromagnetic Waves 150
25 Special Relativity 154
26 Quantum Optics 159
27 Atomic Physics 164
28 Nuclear Physics 168
29 Particle Physics 173

Introduction

The purpose of this Instructor's Guide is to assist you in helping your students learn algebra-based physics using the textbook *College Physics* and the *Active Learning Guide* (ALG). This guide will walk you through the approach we take when we teach, as well as other approaches you might take in using this material in your course. Although both the textbook and the ALG grew out of the Investigative Science Learning Environment, an approach we developed at Rutgers University and California State University, Chico, the textbook itself can work with any curriculum and any instructional approach.

An Effective Approach to Teaching Physics

We believe that one of the important goals of education and higher education in particular is to help students become independent thinkers. To contribute constructively to society, students need to be able to critically analyze information and generate new knowledge based on the assumptions of the physical and social environment in which they operate. Thus, higher education needs to be concerned with more than students learning the "final product of physics." We believe that a student who understands the process of generating knowledge can use this understanding to become a lifelong learner in any field.

These beliefs form the basis for the Investigative Science Learning Environment (ISLE). Students who learn physics in ISLE learn by engaging in the processes of *doing* physics—processes that mirror the way physicists practice physics. First, students observe and analyze so-called *observational* experiments. These observations and analyses lead to the development of physics models and hypotheses. Second, students can use the models and hypotheses to make predictions of the outcomes of *testing* experiments. They then compare their predictions with the actual outcomes. If the models or hypotheses survive the testing, they become the basis for future real-world problems, applications, and testing. If not, students might reject the models or hypotheses. Third, this experimentation and model building leads to the development of what we will term physical theories, such as Newton's theory of universal gravitation or the Kinetic Molecular theory. These three roles of experimentation, from observation to testing to application, form the backbone of the ISLE learning cycle. They also form the structure upon which the textbook and ALG are built.

For students to take ownership of their own learning, they need to develop certain scientific abilities or "habits of mind." We often complain that when encountering a physics problem, students proceed to search for a formula, whereas a physicist in a similar situation starts with a sketch and qualitative analysis of relevant information. This book helps students develop the ability to represent physical processes in multiple ways and thus approach problems in an expert way. We also help students develop the ability to evaluate the reasonableness of a result. Physicists evaluate a result by taking a limiting case. As you look through the ALG and the textbook, you will see that in addition to asking students to solve problems, we include many activities that specifically target the development of these scientific abilities.

Do we have evidence that the ISLE approach helps students learn physics and develop scientific abilities? Over the past 10 years instructors using the ISLE philosophy, the first version of the ALG, and their own ISLE-inspired materials have found that their students not only learned physics concepts (as assessed by physics education research-based tests such as the Force Concept Inventory [FCI], the Mechanics Baseline test [MB], the Conceptual Survey of Electricity and Magnetism [CSEM], and others) but also outperformed traditionally taught students on problem-solving exams, understanding of the nature of science, writing of lab reports, and so on. The list of research papers describing student learning in ISLE-based classes is given at the end of this introduction.

Learning Principles that Serve as the Foundation of the Book

In addition to following the ISLE philosophy, *College Physics* adheres to several important principles.

Principle 1: Concept first, name second—Wherever possible, we try to help students devise an *experiential* understanding of a concept through experimental observations, reasoning, and testing before giving that concept a name. This strategy helps students answer the question "how do I know what I know?" a foundational question in science.

Principle 2: Careful language—We try to use very careful language. For example, we help students understand that force is a physical quantity characterizing an interaction between two objects and is not a property of one object and not a physical entity. To do this, we use the expression "the force that object A exerts on B," not "the force of A" or "the force of A on B." We also avoid using the names of the forces and grammatical constructions that might make students think that forces belong to objects—the weight *of* an object or the tension *in* the rope. We do not use the term centripetal force, so that students do not think that it is a real force. When talking about energy we always talk about the gravitational potential energy of a system, not of a single object. When dealing with thermodynamics we use the word *heating* instead of heat to underline an energy transfer "process" as opposed to a "substance" that an object gains. The goal of this careful use of language is to eliminate unnecessary difficulties that traditional use of words adds to the learning of physics.

Principle 3: Bridging words and mathematics—We introduce physical representations that help students "translate" between the language of words and the language of mathematics. These concrete representations can be used to analyze physical situations and experiments and to solve problems. These representations continue to appear throughout the book. For example, force diagrams are used in Chapters 2, 3, 4, 5, 6, 7, 8, 9, 11, 14, 17, 27, and others. Bar charts (momentum and energy) are used in Chapters 5, 6, 8, 11, 14, 26, 27, and 28. These graphical representations form the backbone of students' problem-solving strategy. The goal of this bridge is to help our students create concrete referents in their minds when they reason about abstract ideas—the same purpose behind placing a picture of an apple next to the word "apple" when teaching a child that word.

Principle 4: Making sense of mathematics—When students devise/derive a new mathematical expression or obtain a numerical result, we stop to ask whether the expression/result makes sense. To answer this question, we evaluate the units, apply extreme cases, or use common sense. We also emphasize the difference between mathematical expressions that define a quantity operationally (operational definitions) and expressions that show how this quantity depends on other quantities (cause-effect relationships). For example, one can define the resistance of a resistor as a ratio $\frac{\Delta V}{I}$ where ΔV and I cannot be changed independently. This is an operational definition, because it provides us with a way to determine that value of the quantity but does not tell why the quantity has this value. The expression $R = \rho \frac{l}{A}$ represents the cause-effect relationship, which demonstrates how the resistivity, length, and cross-sectional area (which can be changed independently) affect the resistance. The goal of making sense of mathematics is to help our students be comfortable with the mathematical language of physics and understand that this way of representing the world must agree with other representations.

Principle 5: Moving away from a plug-and-chug problem-solving approach—To help students avoid searching for an equation in which they insert numbers to get an answer for a problem (so-called plug-and-chug problem solving), we introduce other nontraditional types of problems: *Jeopardy Problems*, in which students are given a math or diagrammatic representation of a problem and asked to work backward or forward to invent the problem; *what can you determine problems*, in which students identify several quantities they can determine from the description of a process and then solve for one or more of these quantities; *design an experiment problems*, in which they invent an experiment to test a physics concept, and many others. Research shows that these problems promote higher levels of cognition and improve conceptual understanding and problem-solving skills.

Organization of the Textbook

The book follows a path from mechanics (force, momentum, and energy for linear motion, and force, momentum, and energy for rotational motion) to fluids and thermal physics and then to electricity and magnetism. The book returns to mechanics by introducing vibrations and waves and then proceeds to the study of light, electromagnetic waves, special relativity, and modern physics. To help students learn, the book reviews each physics idea or concept twice—once qualitatively to understand the phenomena and the second time quantitatively to learn to use the mathematical concept. Finally, at the end of each chapter the students synthesize the new concept and concepts learned by applying them to real-life situations. This logic allows students to use the same idea at least three times in each chapter.

Textbook Elements and How to Use Them

The format of this textbook is flexible and designed to accommodate any teaching style. Students can construct the relevant ideas using several approaches: by performing the activities described in the ALG in a lab or by observing and discussing experiment table activities in lecture and then reading the book at home. Students can also read the book before they come to class and use the videos to view most of the experiments.

Each chapter follows the same format and contains the same elements:

1. **Teaser questions, "be sure you know" questions, and chapter-opening story.** Each chapter starts with three interesting questions that are answered later in the chapter. The "be sure you know" three-item list encourages students to review the most important ideas and skills from the previous chapters that they need for the new chapter. The chapter-opening story is connected to the first interesting question but does not answer it: it expands on the question and provides a hook for the chapter material. Following the story, the first paragraph shows how the knowledge that students developed in the previous chapters is insufficient or incomplete but will be useful for building the ideas in the coming chapter.

2. **Observational experiment tables.** These tables describe simple experiments that students use to devise patterns and later explain them. Many of the experiments exist as videos that students can access via the QR codes in the text or through MasteringPhysics. Students can use these experiments when they need to collect and analyze quantitative data. We suggest that students perform the experiments in a lab, observe them in a lecture setting, or view the available videos and then analyze the data provided in the experiment table.
3. **Testing experiment tables.** These tables describe experiments that can be used to test the patterns or hypotheses that the reader learned about while analyzing the observational experiments. Each table describes one or more experiments, predicts the outcome based on the hypotheses under test, describes the outcome, and concludes whether the hypothesis under test should be rejected or should be kept for the time being. If students are performing testing experiments in a lab, make sure they make predictions based on the hypotheses under test, and not on their intuition, and only then perform the experiment. The same is true if you are doing these in lectures.
4. **Reasoning skill boxes.** Reasoning skill boxes focus specifically on the steps students should take to master a specific physics representation, such as a motion diagram, force diagram, momentum or energy bar chart, ray diagram, and so forth. It is best if you follow the same steps in class when students first learn the representation.
5. **Tips.** The tips are short notes focusing the attention of the students on common difficulties. You can emphasize their importance by asking a question to which a particular tip is the answer.
6. **Worked examples.** These examples follow a four-step problem-solving strategy (sketch and translate, simplify and diagram, represent mathematically, and solve and evaluate) that is adapted to the content of every chapter. For example, in linear dynamics students use motion and force diagrams in the second step, and in geometrical optics they use ray diagrams. The purpose of following the same strategy repeatedly is to help students create effective problem-solving habits and increase their confidence. Almost every chapter has a special "Skills" section where each step of this strategy is described in detail and illustrated for a specific example. All other examples follow the steps but do not provide lengthy descriptions. We suggest that you model problem solving in class using a few worked examples so students see the progression of steps. Skipping steps and using shortcuts make students view every new problem as a completely new challenge and prevent transfer of problem-solving skills.
7. **Conceptual exercises.** These qualitative questions require students to apply the first two steps of the strategy: sketch and translate and simplify and diagram. They do not require calculations, and they help students build multiple representation abilities.

8. **Quantitative exercises.** These quantitative one- or two-step simple exercises focus on mathematical representations and evaluation of the result only. The quantitative exercises employ the last two steps of the strategy. The purpose of these exercises is to help students practice new equations and evaluate their solutions.
9. **End-of-section review questions.** The goal of the review questions is to help students learn how to read a science textbook effectively. Many of these questions ask the reader to explain why a particular statement is true. Such questions have been found to be the most beneficial for reading comprehension.
10. **Putting it all together sections.** Almost every chapter has a "Putting it all together" section that shows students how to apply the concepts that they learned in the chapter to solve problems based on the applications of those ideas. For example, in Chapter 1 ("Kinematics: Motion in One Dimension") the Putting it all together section explores why tailgating is dangerous. In Chapter 14 ("Electric Charge, Force, and Energy") the section discusses the charge separation of a Van de Graaff generator. In Chapter 25 ("Special Relativity") students learn how the clock ticks from GPS satellites enable vehicles on Earth to calculate their position with precision.
11. **End-of-chapter conceptual questions.** These questions are a mix of multiple-choice questions (perfect for using in lectures with a student response system) and open-ended conceptual questions that require deep reasoning. You can discuss some of them in class, letting students work in groups or having a whole class discussion, or assign them for homework.
12. **End-of-chapter problems.** The problems are grouped by textbook sections and marked with asterisks that indicate level of difficulty. Special icons indicate problems with a biological foundation, problems that ask students to estimate (rather than calculate an exact answer), or use drawing techniques in their solution. As discussed previously, several types of problems are nontraditional and do not have only one correct answer. Students should get credit for the reasoning process, articulation of assumptions, and considering multiple possibilities. It is beneficial to solve those nontraditional problems in class at first to show students how to reason and then assign them for homework. The general problems at the end of the problem set are more complex, often require estimations, and may use ideas from previous chapters.

Active Learning Guide

Unlike the textbook presentation, which follows the chronological development of each concept through two cycles—qualitative and quantitative, the ALG is organized by types of activities. Each ALG chapter includes four sections: Qualitative Concept Building and Testing, Conceptual Reasoning, Quantitative

Concept Building and Testing, and Quantitative Reasoning. Each section addresses all of the chapter content with specific types of activities. The first and third sections are activities that follow the ISLE cycle qualitatively and quantitatively. The second section helps students gain facility with reasoning by using qualitative representations. The last section adds mathematics to the mix and includes examples of sophisticated experiments that students use to apply what they have learned. Many of the activities in Sections 1 and 3 can be used in labs and lectures. Section 2 presents activities for lectures and problem-solving sessions, and Section 4 is a mix. We recommend that students bring the ALG to class and work in it and use the textbook activities for homework and independent practice. In most chapters of the ALG, the final part of Section 4 ends with a complicated experiment that you can use as a stand-alone lab.

A list of publications about the use of ISLE in the classroom follows:

1. Brookes, D. T., & Etkina, E. (2010). Physical phenomena in real time. *Science*, 330, 605–606.
2. Etkina, E., Karelina, A., Ruibal-Villasenor, M., Jordan, R., Rosengrant, D., & Hmelo-Silver, C. (2010). Design and reflection help students develop scientific abilities: Learning in introductory physics laboratories. *Journal of the Learning Sciences*, 19, 1, 54–98.
3. Etkina, E., Karelina, A., Murthy, S., & Ruibal-Villasenor, M. (2009). Using action research to improve learning and formative assessment to conduct research. *Physical Review*. Special Topics, Physics Education Research, 5, 010109.
4. Rosengrant, D., Van Heuvelen, A., & Etkina, E. (2009). Do students use and understand free body diagrams? *Physical Review*, Special Topics, Physics Education Research, 5, 010108.
5. Etkina, E., Karelina, A., & Ruibal-Villasenor, M. (2008). How long does it take? A study of student acquisition of scientific abilities. *Physical Review*, Special Topics, Physics Education Research, 4, 020108.
6. Etkina, E., & Van Heuvelen, A. (2007). Investigative Science Learning Environment—A Science Process Approach to Learning Physics, in E. F. Redish and P. Cooney (Eds.), Research Based Reform of University Physics (AAPT), Online at http://per-central.org/per_reviews/media/volume1/ISLE-2007.pdf
7. Etkina, E., Van Heuvelen, A., White-Brahmia, S., Brookes, D. T., Gentile, M., Murthy, S., Rosengrant, D., & Warren, A. (2006). Developing and assessing student scientific abilities. *Physical Review*. Special Topics, Physics Education Research. 2, 020103.
8. Etkina, E., Murthy, S., & Zou, X. (2006). Using introductory labs to engage students in experimental design. *American Journal of Physics*. 74, 979–982.
9. Harper, K., Etkina, E., & Lin, Y. (2003). Encouraging and analyzing student questions in a large physics course: Meaningful patterns for instructors. *Journal of Research in Science Teaching*, 40 (8), 776–791.

10. May, D., & Etkina, E. (2002). College physics students' epistemological self-reflection and its relationship to conceptual learning. *American Journal of Physics*, 70 (12), 1249–1258.
11. Etkina, E., Van Heuvelen, A., Brookes, D. & Mills, D. (2002). Role of experiments in physics instruction—A process approach. *The Physics Teacher*, 40 (6), 351–355.
12. Etkina, E., & Andre, K. (2002). Weekly Reports: Student reflections on learning. *Journal of College Science Teaching*, 31 (7), 476–480.

Kinematics: Motion in One Dimension

In Chapter 1, students will learn to describe motion using sketches, motion diagrams, graphs, and algebraic equations. The chapter subject matter is broken into four parts:

I. *What is motion and how do we describe it qualitatively?*
II. *Some of the quantities used to describe motion and a graphical description of motion*
III. *Use of the above to describe constant velocity and constant acceleration motion*
IV. *Developing and using the skills needed to analyze motion in real processes*

For each part, we provide examples of activities that can be used in the classroom, brief discussions of why we introduce the content in a particular order and use of these activities to support the learning, and common student difficulties.

Chapter subject matter	**Related textbook section**	**ALG activities**	**End-of-chapter questions and problems**	**Videos**
What is motion and how do we describe it qualitatively?	1.1, 1.2	1.1.1–1.1.6, 1.2.1–1.2.4	Problems 1, 3	1.2

Some of the quantities used to describe motion and a graphical description of motion	1.3, 1.4	1.2.5–1.2.7	Problem 7	
Use of the above to describe constant velocity and constant acceleration motion	1.5, 1.6	1.3.1, 1.3.2, 1.3.4–1.3.6, 1.3.8, 1.3.9, 1.4.1, 1.4.2	Questions 5–9, 11 Problems 13, 21, 22, 24, 26, 30, 34, 38, 39, 42, 44	
Developing and using the skills needed to analyze motion in real processes	1.7, 1.8	1.4.3–1.4.14	Questions 12, 13, 15, 16 Problems 55, 58, 60, 64, 68, 72, 74, 76, 78, 82	

I. What Is Motion, and How Do We Describe It Qualitatively?

Because any description of motion depends on the observer, it is important that students begin kinematics by constructing the concept of relative motion and a reference frame. As with all Investigative Science Learning Environment (ISLE) cycles, students start with observational experiments and describe what they see (see the Introductory Chapter for more on ISLE). There are many ways to start teaching this material. You can enact Experiment 1 from Table 1.1 of the textbook in a lecture and have students discuss Experiment 2, or students can begin by working through Active Learning Guide (ALG) activities 1.1.1–1.1.3. Ask them what they think different observers will say about the motion of the object in question. A lively discussion should ensue as students try to resolve the idea that an object that appears to be moving for one observer may appear stationary to another observer. Humans are naturally egocentric, thinking their own reference frame is the preferred one. Once students can see that there is some difficulty in defining motion egocentrically, they are ready to read Section 1.1 of the textbook about the definitions of motion and reference frame. The analysis of physical processes in many parts of the book depends on carefully defined reference frames. It is important to get off to a good start in this first section because of the mathematical description of motion in later chapters, especially when dealing with Newton's laws, the Doppler effect, and special relativity.

In the textbook's Section 1.2, students develop a qualitative method to describe motion—motion diagrams. This is the first of many useful representational tools that students will learn as they progress through the semester. We start this material with ALG activities 1.1.4–1.1.6, which help students describe motion by using dot diagrams that represent the position of an object every second. It is likely (unless you are lucky enough to have extremely well prepared students) that your students do not understand what the words velocity and acceleration mean in physics. If you show them the dot diagrams of the two cars in ALG activity 1.1.5, they are just as likely to say that car 2 has a greater acceleration than car 1 as they are to say that car 2 has a greater velocity than car 1. When you or the students conduct observational experiments like those described in the ALG activities, it is critical that the students try to describe what they see in their own words without trying to throw out "physics-y" sounding words. Thus an appropriate response to "What is different in the motion of cars 1 and 2 in ALG activity 1.1.5?" might be "Car 2 covers a greater distance every second as compared to car 1" or "Car 2 is moving faster than car 1." Dots that get closer together (as in ALG activity 1.1.6) mean that "The object is slowing down." With regards to motion, students generally have excellent physical insight and understand what is going on. The difficult part is to build the bridge between their intuitive physical understanding and the more precise verbal *and mathematical* meanings that we reserve for the words "velocity" and "acceleration" in physics.

After this, students can proceed to the formal motion diagrams that use position dots, velocity arrows, and velocity change arrows—such as those in ALG activity 1.2.1. ALG activity 1.2.1 correlates to the motion diagram skills box at the end of Section 1.2 in the textbook. This skills box summarizes the construction of the diagrams. At home, students can read about a similar experiment in Observational Experiment Table 1.2. Alternatively, you can use the experiments in Table 1.2 in a lecture for students to observe and discuss, and then they can read the textbook at home. The biggest difficulty with motion diagrams for the students is determining the direction of velocity change arrows. This skill is crucial in dynamics. Conceptual Exercise 1.1 helps students with this. ALG activities 1.2.2–1.2.4 and end-of-chapter (EOC) problems 1 and 3 in the textbook help students practice motion diagrams. These can be done in lectures and/or recitations.

II. Introduce Some of the Quantities Used to Describe Motion and a Graphical Description of Motion

Section 1.3 defines the quantities time, time interval, position, displacement, distance, and path length as well as the scalar component of displacement along an axis for one-dimensional motion. The tip about subscripts on page 9 emphasizes their importance. Make sure your students pay attention to this tip. Be sure that students can distinguish between a displacement vector and the scalar component of the displacement along an axis. Students can practice those quantities through ALG activities 1.2.5–1.2.7 and problems in the related EOC section. In addition, the end of the section introduces students to the significant digits that are later practiced in the worked examples.

In Section 1.4, students learn to represent one-dimensional motion using data tables and kinematics graphs. They tend to think of the graphs as sketches of the motion and not as abstract representations of the motion. For example, if an object is on the negative side of the origin and moving toward the origin with positive velocity, they think the object is moving in the negative direction because the graph line is in the negative region. This problem is addressed in part if students develop a correspondence between the graphs and the motion diagrams (see Fig. 1.11). A useful strategy to help students more with this difficulty is to ask them to act out the graph. Another important feature of Section 1.4 is the description of the same motion using two different reference frames (see Conceptual Exercise 1.2). This clearly indicates the importance of having a well-defined reference frame for describing the motion of a particular object. After completing the section, you can now have students try EOC problem 7.

III. Use the Above to Describe Constant Velocity and Constant Acceleration Motion

We use the same approach to help students construct the concepts of velocity and acceleration: they analyze position-versus-time data and define the slope of the position-versus-time graph as velocity (ALG activities 1.3.1 and 1.3.2). The same is repeated for the acceleration—only this time students analyze velocity-versus-time data and the corresponding graph and then define the slope of the latter graph as acceleration (ALG activities 1.3.6–1.3.8). Notice that the terms velocity and acceleration appear in the book only after students construct these ideas using the data (graphs). Sections 1.5 and 1.6 in the textbook achieve the same goal. You can either let students do the ALG activities in labs and recitations and then have a discussion in lecture guided by sections 1.5 (Table 1.7) and 1.6 (Figure 1.21a) or start with the lecture discussion, have the students read the textbook, and then (in recitations and labs) assign ALG activities 1.3.4, 1.3.5, 1.3.8, and 1.3.9. Worked examples 1.4–1.6 help students to analyze different types of motion and to start using problem-solving strategies.

When students plot average velocity-versus-time graphs, they often have difficulty with the idea that the point at which the object is moving with that average velocity is in the *middle* of the time interval under consideration. Be prepared to address this point if students ask questions.

Students often have difficulties with the signs of kinematics quantities. The signs are reviewed in Section 1.6—see Example 1.4 and the tip following it (pages 16 and 17). Pay particular attention to this tip and consider using a clicker question to stimulate discussion in class. Students tend to think that anything that is slowing down has a *negative* acceleration and anything that is speeding up has a *positive* acceleration. It can take a while for them to realize that when an object is speeding up, the velocity and acceleration have the same sign, but when an object is slowing down, velocity and acceleration have the opposite sign. Corresponding ALG activities are 1.4.1–1.4.2. In Sections 1.5 and 1.6, we derive the method of determining the area under a velocity-versus-time graph to find an object's displacement during a particular time interval. It's nice if the students can get through the main ideas of these two sections without too much delay. At the end, ask them to make a summary list of the ideas and then use the list to analyze real processes in the last three sections. ALG activity 1.3.9 achieves the same goal.

There are many questions and problems that you can ask the students to answer and solve during lectures and recitations. The following multiple-choice questions can be used with or without personal response systems: Questions 5, 6, 7, 8, 9, and 11. Students can be asked to solve any of the following problems during lectures or recitations: Problems 13, 21, 22, 24, 26, 30, 34, 38, 39, 42, and 44. One effective way to do this is to present the problem and ask each student to work on it alone. After working alone, they can consult with one or more neighboring students to see if they agree about their work. If not, they can try to reconcile their differences. Finally, you can work through the solution with student input, so the solution seems to reflect their thinking.

IV. Develop and Use the Skills Needed to Analyze Motion in Real Processes

In Section 1.7, students are introduced for the first time to a general problem-solving strategy, a recurring feature that is adapted to different content throughout the book. The strategy involves representing processes in multiple ways—words, sketches, diagrams, graphs, and equations (some or all of these)—and then evaluating the result using one or more of three methods: limiting case analysis, unit analysis, and reasonability of the answer analysis. In addition, encourage students to always check whether the representations they used to analyze the problem are consistent with each other. The multiple representation strategy is emphasized in Equation Jeopardy example problems 1.7 and 1.8, where students are given an equation that describes an unknown process. Students are asked to interpret the equation and use it to construct a sketch of a process that is consistent with the equation, then a motion diagram that is consistent with the sketch and the equation, and finally a word problem that is consistent with all of these representations. Students really need to understand the symbols used in the equations to complete these tasks. Finally, a general kinematics multiple representation problem-solving strategy is outlined in Example 1.9. We illustrate every step of the strategy for a problem described in that example. We repeat the same process in almost every chapter, using the same four steps but adapting for the content in that chapter.

The problem-solving strategy is adapted to free-fall problems in Section 1.8. In Table 1.8, students find that free fall has constant downward acceleration of magnitude $g = 9.8\ \text{m/s}^2$. Help students understand that the acceleration in the vertical direction has a minus sign if the y-axis points up and a positive sign if the axis points down. Also focus their attention on the fact that the acceleration is the same for an object while traveling upward, at the top of the flight, and while traveling downward.

The last section applies the ideas of the chapter to a common, everyday phenomenon—tailgating. Example 1.10 is worth careful analysis. It allows students to connect the abstract representations of the idealized motions that they have studied so far to a real-life situation—the analysis of which is important for saving lives. You can use this problem as a "hook" for the whole chapter. End-of-chapter questions that students can answer (concerning free fall) include Questions 12, 13, 15 and 16. You can ask students to solve one or more of the following EOC problems: Problems 55, 58, 60, 64, 68, 72, 74, 76, 78, and 82. ALG activities 1.4.3–1.4.12 are excellent for recitations, and activities 1.4.13 and 1.4.14 can be used in the lab.

2

Newtonian Mechanics

In Chapter 1, students learned how to describe motion using sketches, motion diagrams, graphs, and algebraic equations. In this chapter, students learn how to explain *why* objects move the way they do and add a new representation to their toolbox—a force diagram. They also learn how to test their ideas, a process that is different in science than in everyday life. This chapter focuses on Newton's laws and their applications to one-dimensional motion. In what follows, we have broken the chapter into five parts, with the early focus on qualitative reasoning and the latter on quantitative problem solving. For each part, we provide examples of activities that can be used in the classroom and brief discussions of the motivations for using these activities.

Chapter subject matter	Related textbook section	ALG activities	End-of-chapter questions and problems	Videos
Sketches, systems and external interactions, force diagrams, and adding forces	2.1, 2.2	2.1.1, 2.1.2	Problems 1, 3	
Developing a conceptual relationship between motion	2.3, 2.4	2.1.3, 2.1.4, 2.1.6–2.1.8, all problems in Section 2	Problems 5, 6a, 7, 11–14, 16	2.1, 2.2

quantities and net force; reasoning qualitatively				
Inertial reference frames and Newton's first law	2.5	2.3.1		2.3
Mass, sum of the forces and acceleration (Newton's second law), component form of Newton's second law, the gravitational force, and applying Newton's second law quantitatively for one-dimensional processes	2.6–2.8	2.3.2–2.3.6, 2.4.1–2.4.9, 2.4.11		2.4
Newton's third law	2.9	2.3.9–2.3.11		2.6

I. A Sketch of a Process, a System, External Interactions with a System, Force Diagrams, and Adding Forces Graphically

For students to understand how changes in motion of an object relate to the sum of the forces exerted on that object, they need more than words and equations. In Active Learning Guide (ALG) activity 2.1.1, students physically experience that they need to push up to hold a heavy ball. This activity leads them to the force diagram as a representation of forces. To draw a force diagram, students learn to choose a system object and identify touching objects and nontouching objects (Earth) that interact with and exert forces on the system object. Be careful here. Students want to say that gravity pulls the ball down; however, gravity is the name of a phenomenon, not the name of the *object* that is exerting the gravitational force. This process is described in Section 2.1, which you can use as a guide for your first lecture. Alternatively, students can do the ALG activity in the lab or recitation and then have a discussion in the lecture. If you start with the ALG activity, students might mention air as the object that pushes down on the ball. ALG activity 2.1.2 helps them test this idea.

In Section 2.1 of the textbook a Skill box helps students learn to construct force diagrams. Follow the steps from the Skill box with the students and emphasize the importance of each step. Then ask students to repeat the process using one of the end-of-chapter questions or problems (for example, problem 1 or 3). Remember that they are not yet completing a problem solution—just learning to represent processes using sketches and force diagrams. Somewhere along the way, you can briefly review how to graphically add forces (Section 2.2) so that students can determine the direction of the sum of the forces exerted on an object. Be sure that students understand that when two objects exert two equal magnitude but oppositely directed forces on the object of interest and those two forces add to zero, the forces can in some cases be ignored. This will be important later in the chapter when applying Newton's second law to the motion of an object on a horizontal surface and justification for ignoring the vertically oriented forces. Use ALG activity 2.1.1 here.

Language use is very important in this chapter. We say: "Object A exerts a force on object B" instead of "Force X acts on object B." The "A on B" language communicates the nature of force as an interaction between two objects as opposed to an entity belonging to the system object—for example, the "weight of an object" or "tension in the rope." We always label each force with two subscripts with no shortcuts. When the force label says $\vec{F}_{\text{Earth on system}}$, we read it as "force that Earth exerts on the system" and not "force of Earth on the system" to underscore that Earth does not have a force. We also do not use the term "gravity" as in the force of gravity. Gravity is not an object and cannot be used as a subscript on a force diagram. It also becomes confusing when students try later to apply the third law: if gravity is what exerts a force on an object, then according to the third law the object should exert an oppositely directed force on gravity (the same reasoning applies to the friction and normal forces).

II. Developing a Conceptual Relationship Between Motion Quantities and Net Force, and Using the Relationship to Reason Qualitatively About Processes

At the beginning of their study, almost all students believe the object's velocity is in the same direction as the sum of the forces exerted on it ($\vec{v} \propto \Sigma\vec{F}$). To address this belief, students can do ALG activities 2.1.3 and 2.1.4 in labs or recitations, or in the lecture you can throw a ball straight up and ask students to draw a force diagram for the ball when it's moving upward, downward, and is at the highest point in its flight. Alternatively, you could slide a block across a table and off the end, where it falls to the floor. Ask students to construct a force diagram for the block just after it has left contact with the table. This could be done as a personal response system question in a lecture class, or have students turn in papers with their responses. Most students will show a horizontal force in the direction of motion plus another force(s). Ask them to identify the other object that is exerting the horizontal force on the ball or block. The key that students need to learn is that if they can't identify the object exerting the force, there probably shouldn't be that force in the diagram. Without doing qualitative activities such as described in Sections 2.3 and 2.4, students may have similar answers at the end of their study as they had at the beginning.

You can also discuss the experiments in Experiment Table 2.1 in the textbook and ask students to identify a pattern based on the outcomes of these experiments: How are the sum of the forces and motion quantities related? Most will find that the only consistent response that works for all three experiments is that the $\Sigma\vec{F}$ from their force diagrams and $\Delta\vec{v}$ from their motion diagrams are in the same direction. Some observational experiments definitely contradict the idea that the velocity is in the same direction as $\Sigma\vec{F}$. In our experience, these observational experiments are not sufficient for students to confidently establish the pattern relating $\Delta\vec{v}$ and $\Sigma\vec{F}$. Thus, the observational experiments are immediately followed by a testing experiment in which students are asked to design an experiment to test two alternate hypotheses: (1) $\vec{v}$ of the object $\vec{F}_{\text{net}}$ always points in the direction $\Sigma\vec{F}$ and (2) $\Delta\vec{v}$ of the object always points in the direction of $\Sigma\vec{F}$. The goal is for students to find a counterexample that shows that either (1) or (2) is not *always* true (ALG activities 2.1.6–2.1.8).

At this point, a special note about testing experiments is in order. If you are trying to follow the logical sequence of observations-patterns-explanations-testing closely by having students think up experiments to test the two preceding hypotheses, then you will discover that students have great difficulty with the idea that they should be trying to *disprove* each hypothesis rather than prove it. A significant portion of your students will suggest pushing a stationary object as a testing experiment. Students need to learn why this is not a good testing experiment. If you ask students to draw the directions of $\vec{v}$, $\Delta\vec{v}$, and $\vec{F}_{\text{net}}$, they should quickly discover that all three vectors point in the same direction. Thus the proposed testing experiment is unable to distinguish hypothesis 1 from hypothesis 2. It helps to encourage students to think about the reasoning process of hypothesis testing as a crime or medical mystery. Many TV shows actually depict the scientific reasoning processes of the protagonists very accurately. Students who are familiar with these TV shows will quickly realize that it is much more productive to disprove an idea than to keep confirming an idea that may indeed be incorrect.

After the students construct the rule connecting the force and change in motion, they can now use motion diagrams, force diagrams, and this new rule relating the directions of the net force and acceleration to reason qualitatively about physical processes (for example, all problems in Section 2 of the ALG) and end-of-chapter problems (for example, problems 5, 6a, 7, 11, 12, 13, 14, 16). Help students understand that if enough information is given to use a motion diagram to determine the direction of the acceleration, you can then construct a force diagram to answer a question about an unknown force. On the other hand, if you know enough to construct a force diagram with the known relative magnitudes of the forces, you can use this information to answer a question about the acceleration direction and the subsequent motion.

III. Inertial Reference Frames and Newton's First Law

We tie Newton's first law to the existence of inertial reference frame observers. Students can do ALG activity 2.3.1 and read Section 2.5 in the textbook, or you can use the material of this section to have a discussion in the lecture. The goal is to apply the rule relating the motion and force diagrams to explain the motion of an object from the point of view of two different observers. For one observer the rule works; for the other it does not. Note that we formulate Newton's first law slightly differently than other textbooks do, emphasizing the importance of identifying the observer. Consider a system that does not interact with the environment or whose interactions with the environment are balanced (the sum of the forces exerted on the system is zero). Only an observer in an inertial reference frame sees this system moving at constant velocity. In this approach, Newton's first law serves as a definition of reference frames for observers for whom the subsequent second and third law would be true. In summary, Newton's second law (an object's acceleration is proportional to the sum of the forces and inversely proportional to its mass) holds true in inertial reference frames. We define the term inertia as a phenomenon in which an object moves at constant velocity when there are no forces exerted on it or when the sum of the forces add to zero. We do not use the word inertia for the property of objects to resist changes in their motion. Instead we we use the term inertness.

IV. Mass, Sum of the Forces and Acceleration (Newton's Second Law), Component Form of Newton's Second Law, the Gravitational Force, and Applying Newton's Second Law Quantitatively for One-Dimensional Processes

In Section 2.6, students construct a quantitative version of Newton's second law, including the introduction of mass. The same process is used in Section 2.3 of the ALG. We suggest that you analyze the situations presented in ALG activities 2.3.2 and 2.3.3 before the students move to the analysis of the quantitative data in activities 2.3.4 and 2.3.5. Similar concepts are described in the textbook, in Section 2.6. Students can use the observational data provided to construct graphs of $\vec{a}$ versus $\Sigma\vec{F}$, and $\vec{a}$ versus $1/m$. These activities can happen as a lecture activity or in a lab or can be assigned as homework. We pay particular attention to making sure students distinguish the dependent variable (acceleration) from the independent variables ($\Sigma\vec{F}$ and m). In other words, the acceleration of an object depends on the sum of the forces exerted on it and on the object's mass. Notice that the way we formulate Newton's second law is different from traditional approaches as we focus on the cause-effect relationship between the sum of the forces and acceleration. We also discuss the difference between an operational definition of acceleration as $\vec{a} = \frac{\Delta\vec{v}}{\Delta t}$ and the relation that explains what affects acceleration: $\vec{a}_{\text{system}} = \frac{\Sigma\vec{F}_{\text{on system}}}{m_{\text{system}}}$. We want the students to understand that while the operational definition of a quantity provides a method of determining its value, it does not explain where the value came from. The cause-effect relation does. We continue to emphasize this difference throughout the book.

Section 2.7 outlines the progression that helps students come up with the expression for the gravitational force that Earth exerts on an object. You can follow a similar progression in class and then assign this section for the students to read and analyze, or alternatively students can do ALG activity 2.3.6 and then read the book.

In all of the problems, we use a multiple representation strategy (Section 2.8) involving a word description of the problem, which is used to help construct a sketch representing the problem process. After choosing a system object, the students should use the system in the sketch to help construct a force diagram. The words in the problem statement are used as best as possible to construct a motion diagram. Students should develop the habit of checking to see that the force diagram and the motion diagram are consistent.

At this point, students learn to use a force diagram to help apply Newton's second law in component form to the problem process. If necessary, they can apply one of the kinematics equations to the process. They use the equations to get a quantitative answer for the problem. Finally, they need to evaluate the answer for units, consistency with the diagrams and sketch, order of magnitude, and its consistency with limiting case analysis. You can do one example for the students and then ask them to work on another problem on their own. When they are finished or get stuck, they can get help or check their work with that of a neighboring student. At the end, you can quickly go through the solution with their input at key parts.

The book includes special problems that support this multiple representation strategy—for example, Jeopardy problems. These problems are similar to the types of questions in the TV game show *Jeopardy*, in which contestants are given the answer to a question and must provide the appropriate question. In an Equation Jeopardy problem, students are given equations that are the applications of Newton's second law and perhaps a kinematics equation to an unknown process. They use the Newton's second law component equations to construct a force diagram and the diagram and kinematics equation to construct a sketch of a process that is consistent with the equations. It is impossible for students to solve Equation Jeopardy problems unless they understand the meaning of the symbols in the equations and the nature of the equations. With algebra-based physics students, such problems are appropriate after students have gotten used to applying the multiple-representation problem-solving strategy in the normal forward direction. Use ALG activities 2.4.1–2.4.8 to help students develop multiple-representation skills, problem-solving skills, and evaluations skills. ALG activities 2.4.9 and 2.4.11 can be used as lab experiments.

V. Newton's Third Law

Students have ideas related to Newton's third law (Section 2.9). They understand that when heavy/light and fast/slow moving objects collide, the effects on the two objects are different. But they often confuse the damage or accelerations of the objects with the forces one object exerts on the other. Students need to reconcile their intuition with the physics approach to the world. The sequence of ALG activities 2.3.9–2.3.11 forms a coherent lab, which we have found to be very successful in helping students to start developing their understanding of the third law. After they do this lab, you might pose the following scenario: A semi-trailer truck runs straight into the back of a stopped car. Which object exerts a bigger force on the other? To answer this question, it is important to consider each vehicle as a separate system. First ask the students to draw force diagrams for the truck and car during the collision, indicate the direction of $\Delta\vec{v}$ for each object (comparing before to just after the collision), and then ask them to compare the directions and magnitudes of the $\Delta\vec{v}$ s. After students have talked to each other, remind them of Newton's second law and ask which object had the larger acceleration. Often at this point, many students go back to the lab experience and realize that the force of each on the other is the same, but the truck's acceleration is tiny compared to the car's acceleration because the truck is so much heavier. It is important that students realize that although Newton's third law may seem counterintuitive, it is consistent with their everyday experience. They simply need to make a distinction between the forces exerted by each object on the other and the acceleration of each object. It is generally a very helpful strategy to ask students, "What is your system?" when they analyze the situation involving Newton's third law. Note that we do not formulate Newton's third law in terms of action-reaction but instead focus on the two forces that two objects exert on each other. The double-subscript notation that we have been using for the forces helps students here tremendously as they learn in the section on Newton's second law that they can only add forces that are exerted on the same object to find the sum in the second law.

3

Applying Newton's Laws

In Chapter 2, students learned to apply Newton's laws in situations in which other objects exerted forces on the object of interest only along the line of motion. Most everyday life processes involve forces that are *not* all directed only along the axis of motion. In this chapter, students learn to apply Newton's laws in component form to these more complex processes. We have broken the chapter into four parts. For each part, we provide examples of activities that can be used in the classroom, brief discussions of the motivation for using these activities, and common difficulties that students experience.

Chapter subject matter	**Related textbook section**	**ALG activities**	**End of chapter questions and problems**	**Videos**
Force components and Newton's second law in component form	3.1, 3.2	3.1.1, 3.1.2, 3.2.1–3.2.4, 3.3.1–3.3.3	Problems 6, 7, 8, 9	
Problem-solving strategies for analyzing dynamic processes using Newton's second law in component form	3.3	3.4.4, 3.4.6, 3.4.7	Problems 5–25	

Including friction forces in the analysis of dynamics processes	3.4	3.3.4–3.3.7, 3.4.5, 3.4.10	Problems 34, 50, 80	3.1, 3.2, 3.3
Projectile motion and applications	3.5		Problem 58	3.6

I. Force Components and Newton's Second Law in Component Form

One way to introduce students to the components is to assign Active Learning Guide (ALG) activities 3.1.1 and 3.1.2, which correlate to textbook Section 3.1. The next step is to help students understand that a force vector can be replaced by two perpendicular vector component forces, which when added graphically equal the original force, that is, $\vec{F} = \vec{F}_x + \vec{F}_y$. Force vectors are difficult to manipulate mathematically. Thus, instead of using vector components, we use scalar components (F_x, F_y). The signs of these scalar components indicate the orientation of the vector components relative to an *x,y* coordinate system. The process for determining these scalar components is summarized in Skill Box 1 in Section 3.1 and illustrated in a concrete way in Example 3.1, which involves three strings pulling on a knot (the system). The three forces that the strings exert on the knot are sketched on a background grid, which makes the components apparent by visual inspection. The components can also be calculated to check for consistency of the mathematical and diagrammatic representations.

After introducing this component method, you might ask students to work on their own on problems 6 and 7 and then check with their neighbors to see if they agree. You can then go quickly through the solution to these problems. Having the vectors on a grid helps the students develop intuition for calculating the force components mathematically. Tell students that in the future, they will not have the grids and will use only the mathematical method for determining the scalar components, which we call simply force components. Use Section 2 of the ALG, activities 3.2.1–3.2.4.

As usual, students label forces with two subscripts indicating object A that exerts a force on object B. Now, we add an additional subscript indicating the *x* or *y* component of the force—for example, $F_{\text{A on B},x}$ and $F_{\text{A on B},y}$. This may seem cumbersome, but students accept it quickly. As noted in Chapter 2, the A on B language communicates the nature of force as an interaction between two objects as opposed to an entity belonging to the system object—for example the "weight of an object" or "tension in the rope."

Example 3.1 serves as a motivation to write Newton's second law in component form as opposed to a vector form (textbook Section 3.2). After reading the summary of the component form, students can practice applying it with the help of Skill Box 3.2. The process is illustrated for a person pushing a box that slides down a vertical wall (see Fig. 3.5 and the accompanying text). This process is again illustrated using a background grid—the last time it is used in the text. Problem 8a,c,e and the corresponding parts of problem 9 are good ones for students' first attempts at using this Newton's second law component equation to solve problems. Alternatively students can start with ALG activities 3.3.1–3.3.3, which correlate to Skill Box 3.2 in the textbook.

II. Problem-Solving Strategies for Analyzing Dynamic Processes Using Newton's Second Law in Component Form

In all of the problems, we use the multiple-representation strategy that was introduced in Section 2.8 and used explicitly again in Section 3.3. Students use the word description of the problem to construct a sketch representing the problem process and to translate the text into the language of physical quantities. After choosing the system, the students draw a motion diagram for the system to help determine the direction of the $\Delta\vec{v}$ vector and then draw the force diagram. The motion diagram helps draw the force diagram, as it shows explicitly the direction of the acceleration. Knowing the direction of the acceleration, students can figure out the relative lengths of the force vectors in their force diagram. Students are often uncertain with which forces they should align their coordinate axes. It is important to keep reminding them throughout this chapter and the next that the best rule of thumb is to align one of their coordinate axes with the *acceleration* found in the motion diagram. This makes it easier to apply Newton's second law in component form. Drawing force lengths on graph paper might be a helpful process here. Students could rotate their graph paper so that they see the "alignment" with a now-shifted x and y axis.

We want students to develop the ability to check for consistency between the force diagram and the motion diagram. In other words, does the sum of the forces in the force diagram align with the direction of the $\Delta\vec{v}$ vector found in the motion diagram? Then they use the force diagram to help apply Newton's second law in component form to the problem process. It is important that students understand that components in the same direction whose values can be positive or negative are always added to find acceleration. If needed, kinematics equations can be applied. Students have to produce the quantitative solution before they plug in the numbers. After students use the equations to get a quantitative answer for the problem, they should evaluate it for units, consistency with the diagrams and the sketch, order of magnitude, and its consistency with limiting case analysis. The unit and limiting cases analysis can be done, when convenient, before the numerical answer.

Students find the idea of a limiting case rather hard to grasp. They will need multiple exposures to it before they become comfortable with it. You can do one example together with the students (for example, worked Example 3.3) and then ask them to do the following Try It Yourself exercise before they work on another problem on their own. When they are finished or get stuck, they can get help or check their work with that of a neighboring student. At the end, you can quickly go through the solution with their input for key parts. At home, students can work through Example 3.2 in the textbook and practice elements of the problem-solving strategy by doing end-of-chapter problems in Sections 3.2 and 3.3 (problems 6–25) and ALG activity 3.4.7.

This problem-solving strategy is used with objects moving on a horizontal surface, but not with other objects exerting forces on the system object at angles above and below the horizontal for the cases of no friction. The strategy is also applied to objects moving on inclines (skiers moving down a hill or being pulled up a hill, people of different mass moving down a water slide, and so on).

These types of problems address two common student difficulties: (1) when there is no friction, the force that the surface exerts on the system is always perpendicular to the surface but not necessarily vertical; (2) students often believe that the magnitude of the normal force equals the magnitude of the gravitational force that Earth exerts on the object mg. The application of the y-component form of Newton's second law (perpendicular to the surface of contact) is used to address this difficulty (see the Try It Yourself part of Example 3.2 and problems 10, 11, and 20).

The final subsection in Section 3.3 involves processes in which two objects are connected together (for example, a modified Atwood machine). As we want students to develop general problem solving approaches, we suggest that they analyze such problems in a general way rather than using problem-specific methods. It helps if students choose separate systems (one for each object) and construct motion and force diagrams for each object, including coordinate axes for each diagram. Then apply Newton's second law in component form for each object. Indicate any constraints that are appropriate (for example, $a_{1x} = a_{2y}$, $T_{\text{String on 1}} = T_{\text{String on 2}}$ ...). Simplify the equations and solve simultaneous equations to answer the question. Here, limiting case analysis is particularly useful to evaluate the final equation used to calculate the answer. For example, what if the mass of object 2 is zero—does the equation then provide an expected outcome? Note that it is helpful to view a pulley as a simple string redirector as opposed to a rotating object. Use ALG activities 3.4.4 and 3.4.6 to help students analyze situations with connected objects and test their reasoning experimentally.

III. Including Friction Forces in the Analysis of Dynamics Processes

Students learn about static friction by conducting (or observing and analyzing) experiments described in ALG activity 3.3.4 or analyzing patterns in observational experiments described in Table 3.1, leading to the expression $0 \le f_{\text{s, Surface on System object}} \le f_{\text{s, max}}$. These experiments are easy to conduct either as whole-class demonstrations or as small-group activities. The expression for the maximum static friction force is based on the patterns found in ALG activities 3.3.5–3.3.6 or in the textbook's Table 3.2. As students often think that it is the mass/weight of the object and not the normal force that determines the magnitude of the maximum static friction force, they test this idea in Table 3.3. It is important that students understand that the surface exerts only one force on an object, and we resolve it into two vector components, the normal component and the parallel component, also know as the friction force. That is why the friction force is proportional to the normal force. Table 3.4 in the textbook completes the experimental foundation for the maximum static friction force law. The static friction force is summarized in the Definition Box in Section 3.4. The application of static friction in walking presents a great opportunity for students to see how the friction model they have developed in the class can be applied to real-world scenarios. ALG activity 3.3.7 is an excellent lab activity to address student ideas about friction.

Student learning of kinetic friction is based on the steps they used for static friction and thus takes little time. It is important to discuss possible mechanisms for friction, from very rough to very smooth interacting surfaces. Snow skier (problem 50) and a wallet pressed against the tilted window of a van (problem 80) are fun applications. It is important to choose horizontal and vertical coordinate axes in the latter problem (the horizontal axis is in the direction of the acceleration and there is no vertical acceleration if the wallet does not slide). You can also assign ALG activities 3.4.5 and 3.4.10 and Equation Jeopardy problem 34 from the textbook.

IV. Projectile Motion and Applications

In Section 3.5, students apply the kinematics equations and Newton's second law to analyze projectile motion. The process starts with simple observational experiments when a person moving at constant speed horizontally throws a ball straight up. To explain why the ball always returns to the hands of the thrower, the students need to hypothesize that the horizontal and vertical motions of the ball are independent. Testing experiment Table 3.6 encourages them to test this idea, and the related video can be used in class to supplement real experiments as the video allows the students to see the process in slow motion.

There are a variety of qualitative questions to emphasize the idea that projectile motion is a combination of constant velocity in the horizontal direction and acceleration due to the downward force Earth exerts on the projectile in the vertical direction (for example, problem 58). Quantitative analysis of projectile motion is pretty traditional. The videotaped experiments allow students to test their solutions instantly.

The goal of the last section (Section 3.6) is to apply what students learn to explain the motion of a car. If you ask students what makes the car move, a common answer is "the engine." However, if the engine is a part of the car, then it cannot exert an external force on the car and thus cannot affect its motion. A detailed analysis of the process presented in the section helps resolve this issue. In addition, students find it particularly difficult to understand how it is possible that the road can exert a static frictional force on the driving wheels of the car *forward* in the direction of the acceleration of the car when it is speeding up. It is instructive to bring a bicycle to class and ask students to discuss with their neighbors, or in groups, the direction of the frictional force of the road on the back wheel (driving wheel) and on the front wheel (nondriving wheel) when the bicycle is speeding up.

Likewise, students struggle to understand how it is possible that the static frictional force exerted by the pavement on a shoe can point in the same direction as the person is walking for the "pushing off" phase of the motion. It is always helpful when students are stuck to ask them how the bicycle wheel or shoe would slip relative to the surface if the friction were not present. Once students have figured all this out, you can challenge them to think about the direction of the frictional force on the wheels of a bicycle or car when the vehicle is slowing down by applying the brakes.

Once students feel comfortable with the idea that static friction can take on different values and different directions on the wheels of the car/bicycle, the class can end with a discussion about how electronic antilock brake systems in cars work. Essentially they work to keep static friction at its maximum value by monitoring when the wheel starts to slip relative to the road surface and modulating the force exerted by the brakes on the inside of the wheel. By doing this, the force exerted by the road on the car wheels is maximized, bringing the car to a stop in the shortest possible distance (Section 3.6).

4

Circular Motion

Chapter 4 presents the greatest challenge students have faced so far: uniform or constant speed circular motion. To introduce the concepts of circular motion, we offer two sequences that take slightly different approaches to this topic. Sequence 1 follows the order of presentation in the textbook, and sequence 2 follows the order of presentation in the Active Learning Guide (ALG). You can follow either sequence using both textbook and ALG resources. The only difference is in the order of presentation.

Chapter subject matter	Related textbook section	ALG activities	End-of-chapter questions and problems
Qualitative analysis of constant speed circular motion	4.1, 4.2	4.1.1–4.1.3, 4.2.1–4.2.3, 4.2.5, 4.2.6	Questions 3, 5, 9, 10
Quantitative analysis of constant speed circular motion	4.3, 4.4	4.3.1–4.3.4, 4.4.1–4.4.7	Problems 3,7, 15, 18, 23, 25, 26, 34, 39, 54
Newton's universal law of gravitation and large-scale circular motion	4.5, 4.6	4.5.1–4.5.4, 4.5.6, 4.5.7	Problems 42, 43, 47, 49, 50, 52, 53, 65, 67

In sequence 1, students begin by learning about a new diagrammatic method for determining the direction of acceleration in 2D motion (textbook Section 4.1, ALG activity 4.2.1). They find a pattern: the object's acceleration points toward the center of the circle. Textbook Section 4.2 presents a hypothesis: The sum of the forces exerted on the object moving in a circle must point toward the center of the circle. (This hypothesis follows naturally from Newton's second law, discussed in the previous chapters.) They can test this hypothesis by conducting the experiments in Table 4.1. (These are the same experiments as in ALG Section 4.1.) Thus, the students realize the relationship between the radial acceleration and the sum of the forces exerted on the object that is moving in uniform circular motion. They can then qualitatively test Newton's second law in the radial direction with ALG activities 4.2.5 and 4.2.6.

In sequence 2, students begin by performing and analyzing three experiments in which objects move in uniform horizontal circular motion (ALG activity 4.1.1). They analyze the situations with force diagrams and build a pattern in which, in each case, the sum of the forces exerted on the object of interest points toward the center of the circle (ALG activity 4.1.2). They develop an explanation or hypothesis that an object *always* requires a net force pointing toward the center of the circle in order for it to move in uniform circular motion. They then proceed to test this hypothesis in ALG activity 4.1.3 by predicting what will happen to a ball rolling around inside a metal ring when a piece of the ring is removed. After this, they learn a new diagrammatic method for determining the direction of acceleration in two-dimensional (2D) motion (textbook Section 4.1, ALG Section 4.2) and learn that an object moving in uniform circular motion is always accelerating toward the center of the circle. The instructor should then point out that this is consistent with Newton's second law. Then students can proceed to test Newton's second law in the radial direction with ALG activities 4.2.5 and 4.2.6.

After following either qualitative sequence described above, students learn to reason quantitatively about circular motion. First, they establish a mathematical expression for radial acceleration (the textbook and ALG Section 4.3) and then apply Newton's second law in the radial direction to various real-life scenarios (the textbook and ALG Section 4.4). Section 4.5 in both the textbook and the ALG develop Newton's law of universal gravitation, and textbook Section 4.6 applies it and circular motion ideas to the motion of satellites and planets in their orbits. We provide brief discussions of the progression of the material, typical student difficulties, and examples of activities that can be used in the classroom in the following sections.

In the first section, we describe the textbook sequence (sequence 1) in detail. If you prefer, you can adapt the description to sequence 2.

I. Qualitative Analysis of Constant Speed Circular Motion

We start in Section 4.1 by helping students develop the diagrammatic method to estimate the direction of an object's velocity change and therefore acceleration during 2D motion (this method was developed by Fred Reif and colleagues). The goal of this method is to build on what students have already learned: how to *add* vectors head to tail. Thus it is conceptually easier for them to think of adding a $\Delta\vec{v}$ vector to the $\vec{v}_\text{i}$ vector to get a *resultant* $\vec{v}_\text{f}$ rather than subtracting $\vec{v}_\text{i}$ from $\vec{v}_\text{f}$ to get a resultant $\Delta\vec{v}$. However, more sophisticated students quickly become comfortable with the idea that subtracting a vector is simply equivalent to adding a $-\vec{v}_\text{i}$. Our experience is that it pays for students to see both ways and choose whatever method they feel comfortable with. It is important that the students draw velocity vectors for the object just before and just after the point at which they want to estimate the direction of acceleration, labeling them properly. If they use the technique in the book, they then determine what vector needs to be added to the initial velocity vector to produce the final velocity vector. This is the velocity change vector, which also indicates the direction of the acceleration of the object.

After introducing the method, ask students to either complete ALG activities 4.2.1–4.2.3 or to apply the method for the constant speed motion of a racecar on a circular track (Example 4.1). ALG activities 4.2.1 and 4.2.3 can readily be turned into multiple-choice in-class clicker questions. For example, you can apply the method in activity 4.2.1 to one point and then ask one-third of the students to apply it to point A, a second third to point B, and the final third to point C. The primary goal of these activities is for students to devise a key pattern: When an object is moving in a circle at a constant speed, its acceleration always points toward the center of the circle. From these activities, students have learned two important lessons. First, even though the speed is constant, there is acceleration because the *direction of the velocity* is changing. Second, for constant speed circular motion, the acceleration points toward the center of the circle. It is worth mentioning at this point that when an object moves in a circular path but not at constant speed, its acceleration will not point toward the center of the circle (building on ALG activity 4.2.3). We discuss this in a later chapter.

The tip before Conceptual Exercise 4.1 is very important. Students have a tendency to draw very small diagrams, which makes it very difficult for them to determine the velocity change arrow. Ask them to make the diagrams larger, and it will help them a great deal. Also, remind them that the tail of the velocity change arrow connects to the head of the initial velocity arrow, and the head of the velocity change arrow connects to the head of the final velocity arrow. Students sometimes draw the velocity change arrow in the opposite direction. It helps to remind them that $\vec{v}_\text{f}$ is the vector that *results from* adding $\Delta\vec{v}$ to $\vec{v}_\text{i}$.

The goal of Section 4.2 is for students to devise and test an explanation for why the acceleration of an object moving at constant speed points toward the center of the circular path. Section 4.2 starts with a hypothesis explaining the radial acceleration of an object moving in a circle at constant speed and proceeds to test this hypothesis in Table 4.1. In this Testing Experiment Table, students test whether Newton's second law applied to circular motion can explain the acceleration of the moving object. First, ask students to draw the force diagrams for the proposed simple experiments before you do them. Then, using Newton's second law and the radial direction of the acceleration, have students predict the direction of the sum of the forces exerted on the moving object. For the first experiment in Table 4.1 (a pail swinging in a horizontal circular path at the end of a rope), their force diagram should indicate that the rope exerts a vertical component force on the pail and a horizontal component force toward the center of the circle. The vertical component balances the downward gravitational force that Earth exerts on the pail. As a result, the net force exerted on the pail is just the horizontal component of the force that the rope exerts on the pail, toward the center of the circle.

The students could analyze other experiments—for example, a metal ball rolling inside a metal ring (Experiment 2 in Table 4.1) or a top view of a rollerblader moving in a circle at the end of a rope. In all of the experiments, the sum of the forces exerted on the object of interest points toward the center of the object's circular path, in the same direction as its acceleration. This analysis is consistent with Newton's second law. Note that the purpose of these experiments is not to do quantitative calculations but to provide simple experiments for qualitative analysis and to connect student learning of physics to their real-life experiences.

Students can then use the graphical velocity technique, force diagrams, and Newton's second law to reason qualitatively about circular motion questions (for example, Questions 3, 5, 9, or 10 at the end of the chapter, or ALG activities 4.2.5 and 4.2.6). Students often add extra forces in the direction of motion to their diagrams—for example, in a force diagram for a pendulum ball while passing the bottom of its swing. They also have a tendency to add an outward pointing force because of the sensation of being pushed outward when they themselves are moving in a circular path (such as being in a car taking a turn at high speed). To deal with these issues, insist that students be able to identify the external object exerting each force. They will not be able to give satisfying answers in either case. We also do not ever use the term centripetal force in the book. It is simply a synonym for the radial component of net force, but when it has a special name it becomes confusing for students. Students tend to interpret centripetal force as an additional force exerted on the object and include it on their force diagrams.

II. Quantitative Analysis of Constant Speed Circular Motion

In Section 4.3, students examine the kinematics of circular motion quantitatively. They analyze experiments (Observational Experiment Tables 4.2 and 4.3) or use ALG activities 4.3.1 and 4.3.2 to develop an expression for the magnitude of the radial acceleration of an object moving at constant speed v in a circle of radius r ($a_r = v^2/r$). The key to ALG activity 4.3.1 or Experiments 2 and 3 in the textbook table is understanding that the acceleration of an object is the ratio of the velocity change over the time interval during which this change occurred. Students tend to focus on the velocity change and overlook the time interval. Make sure students read the analysis (second column) of the experiments in both tables. Also, notice the Try It Yourself question after Quantitative Exercise 4.3 that helps students see the importance of choosing correctly the radius of the circle. To test Newton's second law for circular motion, students can do ALG activities 4.3.3. and 4.3.4.

Section 4.4 applies the component form of Newton's second law, kinematics, and our qualitative reasoning abilities to circular motion problems. Students must learn to use a coordinate system with a radial axis (toward the center of the circle) and for some problems a vertical y-axis. Before doing traditional problems, it is helpful for the students to practice drawing force diagrams and writing Newton's second law without solving for anything. ALG activity 4.4.1 serves this purpose. Again, it is a good idea to use graph paper that students can rotate to assist them in the choice of the coordinate system when they are drawing force diagrams. A problem-solving box outlines the multiple representation strategy for circular motion problems. After reviewing the strategy, students can be asked to apply it to end-of-chapter problems 3, 7, 15, 25, 39, or 54. The section ends by using the strategy on three examples. In all cases the acceleration of the object of interest is in the radial direction, although the vertical y-component form of Newton's second law is needed to complete the solutions. End-of-chapter problems 18, 23, 26, and 34 also require the use of both a radial axis and a vertical y-axis. ALG activities 4.4.2–4.4.6 achieve the same goals. Activity 4.4.7 is a great lab where students can put together what they learned in an experiment.

At the end of Section 4 there is a section entitled "Conceptual Difficulties with Circular Motion" that helps students reconcile their everyday knowledge with what they just learned. Students are invited to analyze the situation of a passenger in a turning car from the point of the view of the observer on the ground or from the point of view of the observer in the car. The latter cannot explain why she/he starts sliding toward the door when the car turns. This means that the car is not an inertial reference frame. This is an excellent opportunity to revisit the circumstances under which Newton's second law holds.

You may want to refer to this section much earlier in the development of circular motion. From early on, more curious students will recognize that the feeling of being "thrown to the left" when you turn right (or vice versa) in a car does not seem to be consistent with the idea that the sum of the forces on the person in the car point toward the center of the circle. This is a great opportunity to turn a lecture into an interactive discussion. You could invite students to turn to their neighbors and discuss how they could reconcile the feeling of being thrown away from the center of the circle with the idea that the net force points toward the center of the circle. It is an opportunity for students to integrate their knowledge of Newton's first law with the idea that even though the speed of an object moving in a circle may not be changing, the *direction* of its motion is changing.

II. Newton's Universal Law of Gravitation and Large-Scale Circular Motion

One of the goals of the textbook is to help students see the origins of the concepts and relations that comprise the body of introductory physics. The approach we took to help students learn Newton's law of universal gravitation is consistent with this goal. Following Newton's own reasoning, students analyze the data for the circular motion of the Moon and compare the Moon's acceleration to the free-fall acceleration of the objects on Earth. Then they apply Newton's second law to explain why objects on Earth fall with the same acceleration (independent of their mass) and thus reason that the force that Earth exerts on an object is proportional to the object's mass. Finally, they use Newton's third law to come up with the idea that the force that Earth exerts on an object should be proportional to the mass of Earth as well. Students at this level can follow this reasoning leading to the force being proportional to $1/r^2$ and the product of the two masses involved Mm. The proportionality constant G was determined after Newton's time. As a testing experiment, students then can use Newton's laws plus the law of universal gravitation to derive Kepler's third law, well known empirically at that time. This logical progression is reflected in ALG activities 4.5.1–4.5.4. You may want students to work on those activities in groups before the whole-class discussion.

In Section 4.6 of the textbook, the law of gravitation along with Newton's second law and the expression for radial acceleration are used to analyze phenomena such as the orbit of geosynchronous satellites and what people refer to incorrectly as weightlessness. End-of-chapter problems 42, 43, 47, 50, 52, 53, and 67 are good practice problems involving the orbits of satellites, planets, and other celestial objects. Problems 49 and 65 address the misleading idea of weightlessness. ALG activities 4.5.6 and 4.5.7 address the same goals.

5

Impulse and Linear Momentum

In the first four chapters of the text, we developed and applied the principles of Newtonian physics; the focus was on forces exerted on objects and on careful description of the details of the resulting motion. In this chapter, we introduce a new approach involving physical quantities that remain constant for a system of one or more objects when the external environment has no net effect on the system. When the physical quantity that describes the system *does* change due to the action of the environment, we can account for that change. This means that the physical quantity is *conserved.*

Section 5.1 illustrates this approach by considering the mass of a system of objects. The remainder of the chapter focuses on the ideas of impulse and momentum. We have broken the chapter into three parts:

I. *Helping students develop the main ideas involving impulse and momentum*
II. *Applying the general impulse-momentum principle to physical processes, including the use of words, sketches, impulse-momentum bar charts (a new representation), and equations*
III. *Applying the impulse-momentum principle and knowledge from the first three chapters to interesting real-life physical processes*

For each part, we provide examples of activities that can be used in the classroom and brief discussions of anticipated student difficulties with the subject matter.

Chapter subject matter	Related textbook section	ALG activities	End-of-chapter questions and problems	Videos
Helping students develop the main ideas involving impulse and momentum	5.1–5.3	5.3.1–5.3.4, 5.4.1	Questions 2, 6, 25 Problems 10–12, 14, 17, 19, 22	5.1, 5.2
Applying the general impulse-momentum principle to physical processes, including the use of words, sketches, impulse-momentum bar charts (a new representation), and equations	5.4, 5.5	5.4.2–5.4.5	Questions 10, 11 Problems 43, 45, 46, 49, 56, 70, 72, 74, 76	
Applying the impulse-momentum principle and knowledge from the first three chapters to interesting real-life physical processes	5.6, 5.7		Problems 20, 40, 57, 58, 60, 62, 63	

I. Students Help Develop the Main Ideas of Impulse and Momentum

Students first meet the idea of a conserved quantity (mass) in Section 5.1. The mass of an isolated system remains constant. If the system is not isolated, mass can enter or leave the system, but this is compensated for by the mass of the environment decreasing or increasing, respectively. This is what makes mass a conserved quantity. The section provides a concrete introduction to this important subject and shows students a useful representation for a conserved quantity: a bar chart. The goal of this section is to help students develop a conceptual understanding of, and representational abilities relating to, conserved quantities so that they can transfer these abilities to the more abstract quantity of momentum.

In Section 5.2, the goal is for students to invent a new physical quantity that is a product quantity. So far, they have used data to invent ratio quantities—the rate of change of position, the rate of change of velocity. This time they have to invent a physical quantity that is the product of two others, which (perhaps surprisingly) is more difficult than a quantity that is the ratio of two others. Active Learning Guide (ALG) activities 5.3.1 and 5.3.2 and the textbook's Table 5.1 describe a series of experiments in which two carts collide. Students need to consider the system as the combination of two carts and analyze and compare the initial and final amounts of different quantities describing that system. They find that the sum of the mass times velocity of all the objects in an isolated system ($\Sigma m\vec{v}$) is the same for both the initial and final states of the system. This sum is given the name *momentum*.

If you are showing students similar experiments in class or are using Videos 5.1 and 5.2, it is important not to say the word momentum before students come up with the concept (this is true for any new quantity). You will notice that no new concept is defined in the book before students have a chance to "construct" it from concrete experience, either by doing and analyzing a real experiment or making sense of provided data. Helping students to create "an image" in the brain prior to providing an abstract definition makes the memories of the concept more accessible. It is also important to recognize that if you let students invent the quantity on their own, they may come up with other quantities that remain constant for an isolated system. For example, for *elastic* collisions the sum of mass times speed of all objects remains constant. Students might come up with this quantity and simply ignore the one (*inelastic*) collision where $\sum mv$ does not remain constant before and after the collision. It is helpful to remind them that they are trying to find a physical quantity that stays the same before and after the collision for *all* possible cases; they are not allowed to ignore one case.

The constancy rule for the momentum of a multi-object system is tested in ALG activities 5.3.4 and 5.4.1 and in the textbook Table 5.2. If you are not using the ALG, encourage students to make predictions before reading the outcomes of the testing experiments in the textbook. Insist that they explicitly use the rule under test when making the predictions. End-of-chapter question 25 is a straightforward multiple-choice problem that could be used to check student understanding at this point.

There are several student difficulties to anticipate:

1. Students need to carefully identify a system and keep track of the initial and final momentum of each object in the system. The system choice is often fairly obvious, but we learn later that choosing a one-object system or a two-object system allows students to answer different questions.
2. Students need to decide if the system can reasonably be considered isolated. Equal magnitude and oppositely directed forces can be ignored, since in combination they do not change the momentum of the system. Friction forces that

surfaces exert on the objects are often small compared to the forces the objects exert on each other during collision processes and can usually be neglected.

3. Momentum is a vector quantity analyzed using the momentum components along each coordinate axis. This requires a well-defined coordinate system and the use of correct signs for the momentum components.

In Section 5.3, students rearrange Newton's second law for a one-particle system to come up with the idea of the impulse that an external force exerts on the system object (ALG activity 5.3.3). They also use Newton's second and third laws to understand momentum constancy for an isolated system. After students see how the momentum constancy idea follows from Newton's laws, it is helpful to emphasize that momentum is not really something new. It is something they have already learned, just reconceptualized in a different language, the language of a conserved physical quantity.

Students can now answer questions 2 and 6, complete ALG activity 5.41, and work end-of-chapter problems 10–12, 14, 17, 19, and 22.

II. Develop Skills to Apply the Generalized Impulse-Momentum Principle in a Way that Leads to Understanding

In Section 5.4, students learn the generalized impulse-momentum principle in vector and component forms. It can be used for any process with an isolated or non-isolated system. They use a new qualitative way to represent such processes—impulse-momentum bar charts. These charts serve a similar role to that played by force diagrams in Newtonian physics. When drawing bar charts, the main difficulties are how to decide what objects are in the system and how to represent the motion of objects described in the problem statement as bars. Students often have trouble with the idea of indicating momentum in the negative direction using downward bars and correctly incorporating external impulses into the bar chart. ALG activities 5.4.2–5.4.4 address those issues.

In addition, textbook Example 5.3 (the happy and sad balls) or matching ALG activity 5.4.5 is a very productive exercise that allows students to wrestle with the difficulties described. First, demonstrate in class the experiment where the sad ball fails to knock over the wooden block, but the happy ball does. In a small studio-class environment you can then ask each group of students to draw a bar chart of the process on a whiteboard with the goal of explaining why the happy and sad balls had different effects on the block. Students will naturally ask whether or not to include the block in the system. You can encourage some groups to treat the ball as the system and other groups to treat the ball and block together as a system during the collision. Either approach will work, and great discussions can follow when they present their work to the rest of the class.

In a large lecture, you can break the exercise into a couple of steps: (1) Ask students to consider the ball as an isolated system and then vote on the correct impulse-momentum bar chart. They should then discuss their votes with each other and vote again; (2) Ask them to do the same analysis considering both the board and the ball as a system. Ask them to vote on the bar chart, then discuss with neighbors, then vote again. In this case it is important to recognize that the board receives some momentum from the sad ball (it rocks back and forth) even though it does not fall over. What students take away from this exercise is not only that the direction of motion matters, but that a bar chart is a tremendously powerful way to analyze a physical process.

Students want to know why there isn't an "initial" and "final" impulse. Students are learning that impulse does not describe a state of the system in the way that momentum does. Momentum "resides" in the system, whereas impulse is the mechanism through which the momentum of the system can be changed—it does not reside in the system. It is ontologically distinct from momentum, and this point must be emphasized. Impulse quantifies a continuous process that adds or takes momentum away from the system from the initial state all the way through to the final state. The shading of the area where students have to place the impulse bar indicates that impulse is a quantity fundamentally different from momentum. On a bar chart, the total height of the bars in the initial and impulse regions must equal the total height of the bars in the final region. To help students with this, we overlay a grid onto each bar chart.

After students learn how to draw bar charts and use them to apply the generalized impulse-momentum equation to a particular process, they can apply this method to end-of-chapter problems such as 70, 74, and 76. The method can also be used to analyze end-of-chapter questions 10 and 11. All of the problems in ALG Section 5.4 can be used too.

In Section 5.5, students learn general problem-solving skills for using momentum to analyze physical processes. Example 5.4 describes a process that students need to analyze. They then represent the process with a sketch. Then they use the sketch to represent the process with a bar chart. Finally, they use the bar chart to apply the generalized impulse-momentum equation to the process.

To determine the impulse caused by the force that an external object exerts on a system object, students will need the time interval that the force is exerted. In the case of an object coming to rest (Example 5.5), often it is the stopping distance that is known, not the time interval the object took to stop. An important method for converting a stopping distance to a stopping time interval is summarized and used in this section. It provides a good opportunity for the students to review kinematics. Students can solve end-of-chapter problem 56 to practice the procedure. Other problems that can be used for practice include problems 43, 45, 46, 49, and 72.

III. The Application of the Generalized Impulse-Momentum Principle and Knowledge Developed Earlier to Analyze Some Interesting Real-World Applications

Jet propulsion is the subject of Section 5.6. It does *not* include the continuous ejection of fuel from a rocket and its continual mass change—a subject that requires the use of calculus. However, it addresses conceptually the common belief that the fuel has to push against something for the rocket to accelerate. End-of-chapter question 9 is a good classroom conceptual reasoning activity.

Section 5.7 has three Putting it all together applications: meteorite impact with Earth, radioactive decay, and collisions in two dimensions. In the meteorite–Earth collision subsection, we use two different systems to answer two different questions. This illustrates how the question motivates the choice of system. Classroom observations show that students have difficulty transferring their physics understanding into a different context, such as a meteorite collision with Earth as opposed to a collision of two carts. Varying the contexts of the situations helps students see the broad applicability of the principle.

Students may be confused about why the force of friction exerted by the surface on the cars is ignored when the cars collide (Example 5.9) or why we don't worry about the gravitational force exerted by Earth on objects when they break apart (Example 5.8). Students should recognize that in collision events the initial and final states of the system are very close together in time. When this is the case, external forces are multiplied by a small Δt, resulting in a small or negligible impulse contribution to the bar chart. This only works if the interaction time is short and/or the external forces are small relative to the interaction forces between the objects that are included in the system.

End-of-chapter problems that can be used in lectures or recitations include problems 57, 58, 60, 62, and 63. Problems that ask students to make a list of the quantities that they can determine using the information given in the problem are particularly useful. They help students consider the relevant physics concepts rather than seeking out an equation that lets them solve for a single unknown. Examples include problems 20 and 40.

6

Work and Energy

In the last chapter, students learned about two conserved quantities—mass and momentum. Here they encounter the idea of the total energy of a system and the means to change it by doing work on the system. Just as the quantity *momentum* is either constant for a system of one or more objects if the system is isolated or can change when an external impulse is exerted on the system, the total *energy* of the system is constant if the system is isolated and changes if an external force does work on it. This approach allows us to incorporate the changes in the internal energy of the system into the generalized work-energy equation and removes the need to discuss conservative and nonconservative forces. As you read though the chapter, you will learn the details of this approach. Here we summarize briefly:

1. To determine the energy of a system, one must first choose a system. Any choice is allowable, but given the objective, often certain choices of system are better than others.
2. Total energy is a property of a system. It describes the interactions between system objects and the motion of the objects in the system. The various forms of energy can be converted from one to another within the system.
3. External objects (parts of the environment) can do work on the system (positive or negative) and thus change its total energy. Objects within the system cannot do work.
4. The energy conversions within the system and the changes of the total energy due to work done by external forces can be represented on a bar chart.

Many physics education research studies have found that students have difficulties differentiating between work and energy and often double count. For example, in a system including Earth and another object (and therefore possessing gravitational potential energy) students will still reason that Earth does work on the system. The approach used in the book not only allows us to address this problem but also helps with the first law of thermodynamics and all other areas of physics in which energy is the primary focus—the photoelectric effect, atomic spectra, fission, and so on. The approach establishes a link not only among different areas of physics but also between physics and chemistry. The idea of energy arises first in mechanics and develops throughout the text.

We have broken the chapter into six parts:

I. *Students develop the main ideas of work and energy* Sections 6.1 and 6.2 help students devise work as a physical quantity, explain the different forms of energy, and introduce a new bar chart to represent work-energy processes qualitatively.

II. *Develop quantitative expressions for the different types of energy*

III. *Apply the generalized work-energy principle to interesting real-world processes in a way that leads to understanding.* Section 6.6 teaches how to use the generalized work-energy principle in a multiple-representation strategy to analyze interesting real-life physical processes.

The last three sections of the chapter focus on special work-energy processes:

IV. *Apply momentum and energy conservation to different types of collisions*

V. *Develop the idea of power as the time rate of system energy conversion from one form to another or the time rate at which work is done on a system*

VI. *Construct a new expression for the gravitational potential energy of a system*

For each part, we provide examples of activities that can be used in the classroom and brief discussions of anticipated student difficulties with the subject matter.

Chapter subject matter	**Related textbook section**	**ALG activities**	**End-of-chapter questions and problems**	**Videos**
Develop the main ideas of work and energy	6.1, 6.2	6.1.1–6.1.3, 6.2.1, 6.2.2	Questions 2, 3, 5, 13 Problems 1, 3, 5, 6, 40, 41	6.1–6.3
Develop quantitative expressions for the different types of energy	6.3–6.5	6.3.1–6.3.3, 6.3.5, 6.4.1–6.4.3	Questions 9, 10 Problems 10, 11, 15, 18, 22, 23. 25, 30, 31, 33, 34, 35, 37	
Apply the generalized work-energy principle to interesting real-	6.6	6.4.4–6.4.11	Problems 24, 28, 29, 32, 42, 43	

world processes in a way that leads to understanding				
Apply momentum and energy conservation to different types of collisions	6.7		Question 12 Problems 48. 49, 51	6.6
Develop the idea of power as the time rate of system energy conversion from one form to another or the time rate at which work is done on a system	6.8		Problems 59, 61, 62, 63	
Construct a new expression for the gravitational potential energy of a system	6.9		Problem 70	

I. Students Develop the Main Ideas of Work and Energy

Active Learning Guide (ALG) activity 6.1.1 and Observational Experiment Table 6.1 lead students through four simple experiments in which a carefully defined system (Earth is part of the system) either gains the ability to break a piece of chalk or becomes warmer. Observational Experiment Table 6.1 matches the ALG activity but includes the answers. These experiments are easily reproduced in a lecture setting. (When we teach the material, we have students use the ALG table first and then read the answers in the textbook at home.) Students analyze the experiments by indicating the direction of an external force (represented by an arrow) exerted on one of the objects in the system as it moves from an initial state to a final state as well as the direction of the object's displacement (also represented by an arrow). They see a pattern: when the chalk-crushing ability of the system increases, the force and the displacement are in the same direction. Positive work is said to be done on the system, causing something in the system to increase so it could break the chalk or become warmer. This "something" that changes in the system when work is done on it is called energy.

The book *does not* define the total energy of a system as the ability to do work but instead as the sum of the different types of energy that change when work is done on the system. Energy comes in different forms, such as gravitational potential energy, kinetic energy, elastic potential energy, and internal energy (the warming and structural changes of objects). Other forms of energy (electric potential energy, rest energy, and so on) will be encountered later in the book and seamlessly fit into the framework developed in this chapter.

ALG activities 6.1.2 and 6.1.3 and Observational Experiment Table 6.2 help students extend their understanding of work to the cases of negative and zero work. They read (or perform and analyze) three experiments in which the system either loses some of its ability to break the chalk or its ability does not change. The students' analysis of the force arrow and the system displacement arrow indicates that the arrows are in the opposite directions or perpendicular to each other, respectively. In the first two of these three experiments, negative work is said to be done, whereas in the third experiment (perpendicular force and displacement) zero work is said to be done. The patterns identified in Tables 6.1 and 6.2 lead to a formal definition of work: $W = Fd\cos\theta$. It is helpful to point out to students how using the cosine function captures all the features of positive, zero, and negative work that they found in the observational experiments.

Students experience two difficulties with the concept of work. The first is linguistic. Many times, students will ask, "how is it possible that I can hold a heavy object in my hand and yet I am doing no work according to the definition?" It helps to remind students that physicists have simply reappropriated an everyday word into physics, and that in physics, "work" has a much more specialized meaning than in everyday language. (Also, in the above example, physics does not consider the "microscopic" work done by the contracting muscles supporting the object.) The second difficulty is that the abstractness of the mathematical expression for work can very often lead students to forget the physical meaning of the mathematical expression and revert to "plug-n-chug" approaches. Try posing problems 1 and 3 from the back of Chapter 6 as clicker questions in a large class or for group discussion in a studio classroom.

We defined energy of a system as something that changes when external objects do work on the system. The logical consequence of such definition is the hypothesis that the energy of an isolated system is constant. Students test this hypothesis by doing and analyzing experiments described in Testing Experiment Table 6.3 in Section 6.2 (experiments in Table 6.3 can be done in a whole-class setting or in a lab setting). They then learn to analyze processes in which work is done on the system using qualitative work-energy bar charts. A bar chart has initial and final bars for each type of energy of the system. These are separated by a central shaded region for one or more bars representing the work done on the system by external objects. The bar chart can then be translated into an equation:

$$U_{\mathrm{i}} + W = U_{\mathrm{f}}$$

$$(U_{\mathrm{g\,i}} + K_{\mathrm{i}} + U_{\mathrm{s\,i}}) + W = (U_{\mathrm{g\,f}} + K_{\mathrm{f}} + U_{\mathrm{s\,f}} + \Delta U_{\mathrm{int}})$$

Table 6.4 provides examples of processes in which energy is converted from one form to another and represents these conversions with bar charts. Corresponding activities in the ALG are activities 6.2.1 and 6.2.2.

A Reasoning Skill Box on page 193 describes how to construct the bar charts and helps students apply bar charts to more complex problems. Encourage students to explicitly go through all of the reasoning about a physical situation by constructing a bar chart for the process (choosing the system, defining initial and final states, and considering what energies the system possesses in each state). They can later convert the information in the chart to the mathematical form of the work-energy principle. A couple of bar chart activities in class provide a great opportunity to generate discussion among students as they try to make sense of what they are doing. The advantage of using the bar charts is that students can analyze any process qualitatively without overburdening their minds with mathematical symbols in an equation—symbols that may have little meaning to them at this early stage. Research shows that this qualitative reasoning leads to better intuitive understanding of work and the changes of different types of energy, and ultimately leads to superior reasoning and problem-solving ability.

There are several important issues to consider: (1) Students have difficulties choosing initial and final states of the process. Help them by explicitly asking every time they start a new problem what initial and final stages of the process they wish to consider; (2) They need to choose a system. For work-energy processes it is often advantageous to choose a fairly large system so that all the energy changes are internal to the system rather than expressed as work done by external objects. Table 6.4 provides simple examples of such system choices. You can ask students to construct bar charts for these or other examples. Use simple ones at the beginning; (3) It is usually easiest to include the gravitational interaction between Earth and an object as gravitational potential energy. To do this, Earth must be included in the system. However, if Earth is not included in the system, the object by itself does not have any gravitational potential energy, and gravitational interaction is expressed as work done by Earth.

Students struggle with the idea of choosing a zero point for gravitational potential energy of an object-Earth system. It helps to go through explicit examples in class. For example, holding a marker in your hand, one can ask students to discuss how much gravitational potential energy the system (marker and Earth) has relative to the instructor's desk as opposed to the floor. In trying to resolve this issue, students will come to recognize that they always need to choose an explicit zero point when discussing gravitational potential energy. In addition, thinking about gravitational potential energy of an object-Earth system, students reevaluate their experience of the physical world. An object on its own does not possess gravitational potential energy. An increase in gravitational potential energy arises from the fact that the instructor (an external agent) moved the marker and Earth farther apart from each other. When the marker and Earth fall back together, they are able to crush chalk between each other. Most students probably have not thought about the idea that Earth "falls" toward the falling marker. Please note that in this initial encounter with energy, we ignore processes involving friction until Section 6.5. Students can now answer questions (for example, end-of-chapter questions 2, 3, 5, and 13) and work through problems (for example, end-of-chapter problems 3, 5, 6, 40, and 41).

II. Develop Quantitative Expressions for the Different Types of Energy

ALG activity 6.3.1 and textbook Section 6.3 show students how to derive quantitative expressions for the gravitational potential energy of an object-Earth system and for kinetic energy. ALG activity 6.3.2 and textbook Section 6.4 lead students to Hooke's law by analyzing spring data and then use it to derive the expression for elastic potential energy. We use the same approach in each derivation: Choose a system in which only the needed type of energy changes when external forces do work, and derive an expression for this work that depends on quantities describing the initial and the final state of the system. The sections describe the systems and external forces we chose step by step.

The approach for including friction is a little different than some other textbooks (ALG activity 6.3.3 and textbook Section 6.5). Typically a surface that exerts a friction force on a system object is excluded from the system, and we consider the work done on the system by this surface (an external object). This approach is fine if the system object can be considered a point-like object that does not have internal energy. But in most real processes (for example, a car or skier skidding to a stop), we cannot consider the skidding object as a point-like object. The friction force exerted on the object causes the contacting surface to warm and possibly have structural changes—like scraping some rubber off a car tire. There are internal energy changes in the system object and similar changes in the surface exerting the friction force. We can avoid these difficulties if we include both contacting surfaces in the system; thus we never talk about the work done by friction. Instead, we consider how much work is done by an external agent on the object-surface system in order to keep the object moving at a constant velocity over some distance s. By making this choice, we can consider friction as an internal mechanism that increases the system's internal energy:

$$\Delta U_{\text{int}} = +f_k s$$

rather than considering it as a force exerted by an external object. Here s is the distance the object travels across the other surface. Most students accept this easily as they are not familiar with any other method. Students can do ALG activity 6.3.5 as a lab experiment to test the concept of energy conservation.

Students can immediately apply the outcomes of these derivations to ALG activities 6.4.1–6.1.3 and textbook end-of-chapter problems such as 10, 11, 15, 18, 22, 23, 25, 30, 31, 33, 34, 35, and 37. They can also use the method to analyze end-of-chapter questions 9 and 10. The real fun, however, is in the next part of the chapter, where students apply the generalized work-energy principle to interesting problems. The work-energy approach makes it much easier to solve the same problems that students solved earlier in the course using Newton's second law and kinematics. Additionally all of the videos of the experiments that we used in the Newton's law chapters can be reanalyzed here with the work-energy approach.

III. Apply the Generalized Work-Energy Principle to Interesting Real-World Processes in a Way that Leads to Understanding

Section 6.6 introduces students to problem-solving strategy for the situations where the generalized work-energy principle is applicable (Example 6.6). After the first example, students use the same approach to solve four interesting worked examples: the launch of a human cannonball, a paratrooper landing in a snowbank when his parachute did not open, the stretching of the aorta when blood is pumped into it by the heart, and bungee jumping. End-of-chapter problems that can be used in lectures or recitations include problems 24, 28, 29, 32, 42 and 43 and ALG activities 6.4.4–6.4.10. A good final lab for the energy chapter is in ALG activity 6.4.11.

IV. Apply Momentum and Energy Conservation to Different Types of Collisions

Energy and momentum are used to analyze three different types of collisions in Observation Experiment Table 6.6 in Section 6.7. The collisions involve different types of pendulum balls hitting carts of different rigidity. In each collision, the system is the ball and cart; the system can be considered isolated. Students find that momentum is constant in all of the collisions, but kinetic energy is constant in only the collision in which the pendulum ball and cart results in no structural changes in either of the system objects. From those observations, three types of collisions emerge and are summarized in Table 6.7. It is good to go through these different types of collisions with students and to emphasize that they can use momentum constancy during all collisions.

Deciding at what point to use energy and when to use momentum in an example like 6.10 is one of the most difficult challenges for the students. They can practice analyzing multistep problems involving both energy and momentum using the example of the ballistic pendulum in Example 6.10 and end-of-chapter question 12 and problems 48, 49, and 51. Students need multiple exposures to problems like these before they are able to tackle them with confidence. Students could attempt one of these problems in lecture, another in recitation, and again in homework. Simply telling students that they have to use momentum in an inelastic collision because they cannot account for all the energy will not have much effect on their understanding. The best way for students to build understanding is for them to explicitly draw energy *and* momentum bar charts for the collision part of the problem and then discuss their bar charts with each other. By exposing and resolving the conceptual issues associated with these multistep problems themselves, students will slowly become comfortable to tackle these problems on their own.

V. Develop the Idea of Power as the Time Rate of System Energy Conversion from One Form to Another or the Time Rate at which Work Is Done on a System

Notice that we define power as the rate of conversion of the system's energy from one form to another. That is why the language here is "the power of a process." It is important to emphasize that power is also a rate (ratio-type) quantity, similar to velocity and acceleration—the rate of energy conversion. The concept of power in Section 6.8 is primarily used later in the course—especially in Chapter 17—for electric circuits. There are two worked examples—Example 6.11 for calculating the power during a dead lift and Example 6.12 for the power of an automobile needed to overcome air drag and rolling resistance, and also in going up a hill. Problems 59, 61, 62, and 63 could be used in lectures or recitations for student practice.

VI. Construct a New Expression for the Gravitational Potential Energy of a System

Section 6.9 introduces students to a new expression for gravitational potential energy of a system to be used when g cannot be considered constant. Here the system approach to work-energy problems is especially important. If we consider the gravitational potential energy of two objects separated by an infinite distance to be zero, then an external force has to do positive work in order to slowly separate two initially closely positioned objects so that the distance between them is infinite (this positive work brings the final energy of the system to zero). Representing this process with a bar chart yields the conclusion that the initial gravitational potential energy of two objects separated by a distance less than infinity is negative.

This is a challenging idea for students. It is helpful to begin Section 6.9 with a clicker or discussion question in class. The question presents students with two configurations of a pair of planets. In configuration A, the planets are close to each other; in configuration B, the same two planets are farther apart from each other. The question is, "Which configuration has the greater gravitational potential energy?" Students find this question surprisingly difficult, and it will engender a lively and productive discussion. Many students will incorrectly say that configuration A has greater gravitational potential energy because the force between the planets is greater. Given the opportunity and time, most students can resolve this confusion by discussing it with their peers.

The derivation of the expression for gravitational potential energy when the objects are far apart involves the use of calculus; thus the book outlines the procedure but does not go into mathematical detail. To help students reconcile the final expression for gravitational potential energy of two objects

$$U_g = -G\frac{m_E m_O}{r_{E \to O}}$$

(with zero potential energy when infinitely far apart) with the familiar $U_g = m_O g y$, they compare the work needed to lift 100-kg of supplies to the International Space Station using both methods and find the results to be very close. The idea that the energy zero point is when the objects are infinitely far apart requires radical conceptual restructuring for students who have become familiar with $U_g = m_O g y$. Practicing drawing bar charts for different scenarios will greatly help students make the transition. Later, students will apply the new expression to derive an expression for escape speed and learn about black holes. Perhaps the best reason for introducing this subject is its mathematical similarity to the expression for electrical potential energy that students will encounter in Chapter 14.

Note that students often have considerable difficulty understanding situations where the electric potential energy of a system is negative. They will have a better chance if their first exposure happens in the context of the more familiar gravitational interaction. Problem 70 is good for use in lectures and recitations to help students get used to the idea.

7

Extended Bodies at Rest

Chapters 5 and 6 developed and applied work-energy and impulse-momentum conservation principles. In the work-energy chapter, we started moving away from modeling system objects as point-like objects as we wanted to incorporate the internal energy changes of these objects—for example, during collisions. In this chapter, we start a new approach involving rigid extended bodies (not point-like) that are in static equilibrium. We have broken the chapter into four parts:

I. *A qualitative introduction to rigid bodies and to the idea of center of mass*
II. *The development of the idea of torque and the conditions (translational and rotational) for the static equilibrium of rigid extended bodies*
III. *A quantitative method for determining an object's center of mass*
IV. *The techniques and skills needed to apply equilibrium conditions to interesting examples, including the biomechanics of the human body. This part also includes a section on the stability of equilibrium.*

For each part, we provide examples of activities that can be used in the classroom and brief discussions of anticipated student difficulties with the subject matter.

Chapter subject matter	Related textbook section	ALG activities	End-of-chapter questions and problems	Videos
Develop a qualitative introduction to rigid bodies and to center of mass	7.1	7.1.1–7.1.3, 7.2.1–7.2.3		7.1, 7.2

Develop the idea of torque and the conditions for the static translational and rotational equilibrium of rigid bodies	7.2, 7.3	7.3.1–7.3.7, 7.3.9	Questions 7, 9 Problems 1, 4, 6, 7, 8, 17, 18, 23, 24, 25, 26, 27	7.4
Develop a quantitative method for determining an object's center of mass	7.4	7.3.7	Problem 36	
Develop the techniques and skills needed to apply equilibrium conditions to interesting examples including the biomechanics of the human body	7.5–7.7	7.4	Question 3 Problems 40, 41, 44, 45, 46, 47, 48, 58, 66	7.6

I. Develop a Qualitative Introduction to Rigid Bodies and to Center of Mass

The chapter starts by introducing students to a new model of an object, a rigid body, early in Section 7.1. One of the main properties of a rigid body is its center of mass. To come up with this concept, students can do Active Learning Guide (ALG) activities 7.1.1–7.1.3 in a lab or lecture and then read through a simple observational experiment described in the textbook's Table 7.1. The first experiment involves pushing a flat board on a smooth surface with a pencil eraser (see Table 7.1). Students find that if they push along certain lines through the board, the board slides without turning. The intersection of these points is the center of mass of the board. This idea is tested in Table 7.2. Next, students can observe by experimentation or through a lecture demonstration that the board with the pencil eraser under the center of mass balances. After the experiment, you can summarize for the students that the outcome suggests that the entire gravitational force that Earth exerts on the board can be thought of as being exerted on the board at its center of mass. This is a very important idea used later when applying the conditions of static equilibrium to extended bodies. Students can practice these ideas by doing ALG activities 7.2.1–7.2.3 in recitations and labs.

II. Develop the Idea of Torque and the Conditions for the Static Translational and Rotational Equilibrium of Rigid Bodies

ALG activities 7.3.1–7.3.5 and textbook Section 7.2 help students develop the idea of the torque produced by a force exerted on an extended body as they observe simple experiments involving several spring scales exerting forces on a meter stick at various locations perpendicular to the stick. Students observe patterns in the strength and locations of the pulling forces that cause the stick to remain at rest. If you start torque in a lab or recitation, then students can do the ALG activities and collect their own data. If you start in a lecture, they can use the data in Figure 7.6 in the textbook. The next step is to include the angle between the forces and the stick—students observe and analyze the effect of the angle by doing ALG activities 7.3.6 and 7.3.7 (they need to collect their own data there) or by analyzing the data provided in the textbook's Table 7.3. They devise an expression for the turning effect of a force exerted on the stick (the *torque* that the force exerts on the object):

$$\tau = \pm F l \sin\theta$$

Note that in this book we incorporate the vector nature of the torque through the sign rather than using the cross product. We also do not use the term lever arm, as this is additional (somewhat obscurely named) terminology that often confuses students. As students "invent" the definition of the torque, slowly adjusting it to fit multiple experiments, the process helps them differentiate between force and torque. Finally, the torque represents another product quantity, similar to momentum. Several aspects of using the above equation are very important: (1) Students need to construct an extended body force diagram that incorporates the points at which forces are exerted on the object; (2) Students need to carefully define an axis of rotation even if the object is not rotating. This is needed to determine the distance l that appears in the expression for the torque produced by each force exerted on the extended body. A subsection early in Section 7.2 focuses on the importance of defining an axis of rotation; (3) Students often have difficulty deciding the sign of a torque. A tip toward the end of Section 7.2, just before Example 7.2, provides a concrete method to determine the sign. It is worth going over this method in the tip as a short interlude in a lecture. Recitation instructors should also be taught the method and encourage students to use it.

The experiments in Section 7.2 used to develop the idea of torque also lead to a first introduction to the condition for rotational equilibrium of an extended body. In Section 7.3, students develop the first and second conditions of static equilibrium further (see Tables 7.4 in Section 7.3). Here, it is important to discuss with the students the difference between force and torque again, as they often confuse those two physical quantities. Students can test these conditions by working though the experiment in Example 7.3, either as a demonstration in lecture or by performing the experiment in lab.

In lecture, students can first work individually and use the equilibrium conditions to predict the readings on two scales supporting a beam at its ends while a massive block rests off-center on the beam. After students make their initial predictions they can compare their results with those of neighboring students. After the groups agree on their predictions, the instructor performs the experiment so that students can compare their predictions to the experiment's outcome. It is an exciting example of how physics principles can be used to make accurate predictions. In the text, student read about predictions made using two different axes of rotation, an important reminder to carefully choose the axis of rotation. Although the result will be the same regardless of choice, usually certain choices of axes will make the problem easier to solve. Alternatively, students can test the conditions of equilibrium in a lab using ALG activity 7.3.9. End-of-chapter problems such as 1, 4, 6, 7, 8, 17, 18, 23, 24, 25, 26, and 27 and question 9 allow students to practice the method.

III. Develop a Quantitative method for Determining an Object's Center of Mass

Section 7.4 introduces students to a method to quantitatively determine the center of mass of a multiple-point object system and, in principle, of a continuous rigid body. The latter generally requires the use of calculus and is not done in the book. The key concept that the students learn in this section is that the term "center of mass" is often misleading, as the mass of the object is not necessarily symmetrically distributed around the center of mass. Instead it should be called a "center of torque." As many students take the term center of mass literally, it is important that they work though the subsection "Mass Distribution and the Center of Mass," including Conceptual Exercise 7.5. Another example might include a baseball bat, a broom, or any other object with an asymmetrical mass distribution. In a lab, you can take a meter stick, attach a small but heavy object to one of its ends, and then ask students to calculate the center of mass of the combined system. After the students do this, you can ask them if the mass of the system to the left of the center of mass is equal to the mass of the system to the right. If they answer that they are, you can ask them how they can check this answer. Students have no trouble coming up with the way to do it, and they become very surprised to find those masses unequal. Problem 36 addresses this issue. ALG activity 7.3.7 is a good laboratory activity to help students see that the mass of an object is not symmetrically distributed around the center of mass.

Also note that observant students will likely (given the opportunity) ask some variant of the following question: "If I add a new object to a rigid body (e.g., a see-saw) and the question asks, 'where must I move the pivot so that the system balances again?' should I treat this new object as exerting a torque or should I think of it as shifting the center of mass to a new location?" Allowing students to work through and resolve this question can be a great learning experience. At the end, students should realize that the two views are equivalent (assuming you're on the surface of Earth), but, as they have been learning throughout previous chapters, it is all about how we choose the system. If we take our system as the rigid body and think of the new object as external to that system, then we say it exerts a torque on the rigid body. If we choose the new object as part of the rigid body system, then we can say that the center of mass of the rigid body has moved.

IV. Develop the Techniques and Skills Needed to Apply Equilibrium Conditions to Interesting Examples, Including the Biomechanics of the Human Body

Textbook Sections 7.5 and 7.7 as well as ALG Section 7.4 adapt the standard multiple representation problem-solving strategy for solving problems involving static equilibrium. We place considerable emphasis on biomechanics: the biceps muscle lifting the arm, the Achilles tendon lifting the heel of the foot off the ground, and the back muscle lifting a load while in a bent position.

When solving these and other problems in these sections, it is important to emphasize to the students that the same three aspects of the problem solving, described previously in Section II, are important: (1) To construct an extended body force diagram. Note that students have great difficulty in including the force exerted by the hinge/joint on the object/bone of interest. It is also not always obvious in what direction that force is pointing. Students need considerable practice with this; (2) To carefully define an axis of rotation even if the object is not rotating; (3) To choose the correct signs of torques—see the tip on page 238.

The issue of the directionality of torque is probably the most tricky conceptual hurdle that students struggle with in this chapter. Although you or recitation instructors may have used the page 238 tip and introduced the idea of clockwise and counterclockwise, students will naturally use what is familiar to them. Thus students may want to assign a + sign to torques due to upward pointing forces and a – sign to torques due to downward pointing forces. Some students may alternatively want to suggest that torques to the left of the pivot balance torques to the right of the pivot irrespective of the direction of the force.

A good way to help students feel more comfortable with the new concept of clockwise and counterclockwise directions is to present them with the following PRS question in lecture: Give students an extended body force diagram for a uniform beam pivoted about its center. The diagram should show two forces to the left of the pivot, one pointing upward and one pointing downward, and two forces to the right of the pivot, one pointing up and one pointing down. Then ask students to find the signs of the four torques due to these four forces. Give students a chance to revise their responses by talking to their neighbors. A lot of productive discussion and learning will result.

A fourth aspect not discussed yet is the importance of the distinction between torque and force, which students often confuse. In the case of static equilibrium it is important that the students examine whether the forces add to zero along the x-axis and independently along the y-axis (the signs of the force components depend on the chosen coordinate system). Each force can also produce a torque on the extended body, the sum of which students need to examine independently. The signs of the torques are given by hints (see p. 238)—in which way the force tends to rotate the extended body about the axis of rotation (+ for counterclockwise and – for clockwise).

The following questions and problems can be used with students in recitations and lectures: Question 3 and problems 40, 41, 44, 45, 46, 47, 48, 58, and 66. More practice can be found in Section 4 of the ALG. This section also offers suggestions for the lab activities (ALG activity 7.4.7).

Section 7.6 concerns the stability of equilibrium. From the Observational Experiment Table 7.5 students find that an extended body does not tip if it rests on a surface, and a vertical line passing through the object's center of mass passes between the bottom supports of the object. This rule explains why a standing person might fall when a train leaves a station. They consider the experiments to test the rule for a partially full soda can in the Testing Experiment Table 7.6. Another rule that accounts for stable equilibrium is whether or not an object's center of mass is below a fixed axis of rotation.

8

Rotational Motion

In Chapter 7, students learned to analyze situations in which rigid extended bodies were in equilibrium (constant rotational velocity, often zero) despite many forces being exerted on them and producing torques. In this chapter, we analyze situations in which the rotational velocity of rigid bodies changes. The chapter is broken into four parts:

I. *A kinematics description of rotational motion*
II. *A dynamics explanation of rotational motion: a relationship between the net torque exerted on an extended body, the rotational acceleration of the body, and its rotational inertia.* This is all put together into a rotational version of Newton's second law.
III. *A development of the ideas of rotational momentum and rotational kinetic energy*
IV. *The techniques and skills needed to apply rotational motion concepts to interesting everyday examples.* We do this in a putting-it-all-together section, Section 8.7, in which the previous ideas are applied to everyday phenomena.

For each of these parts, we provide examples of activities that can be used in the classroom and brief discussions of anticipated student difficulties with the subject matter.

Chapter subject matter	Related textbook section	ALG activities	End-of-chapter questions and problems	Videos
Kinematics description of rotational motion	8.1		Problems 3, 4, 5, 6, 9, 17	
Dynamics explanation of	8.2–8.4	8.1.1–8.1.5, 8.2.1, 8.2.2,	Question 3 Problems 18,	8.2

rotational motion		8.3.1, 8.3.3, all of 8.4	20, 21, 22, 23, 24, 26, 27, 28, 29, 31, 34	
Development of the ideas of rotational momentum and rotational kinetic energy	8.5–8.6		Questions 7, 10, 12 Problems 43, 45, 47, 50, 52, 55, 57	
Techniques and skills for applying rotational motion concepts to everyday examples	8.7	8.4	Problems 39, 72, 73	

I. Kinematics Description of Rotational Motion

Section 7.1 introduces students to the kinematics quantities rotational position, rotational velocity, and rotational acceleration, as well as to the relationships of the quantities with each other. As in Chapter 7, we assume that a torque that tends to cause counterclockwise rotation is positive and a torque that tends to cause clockwise rotation is negative. The same sign convention applies to the resulting rotational acceleration. Students often have problems determining the sign of rotational acceleration, just as they have trouble determining translational acceleration for translational motion. It is often easier for them to understand that when rotational velocity in the positive counterclockwise direction is increasing in magnitude, the rotational acceleration is also positive.

The situation in which the rotational velocity in the positive counterclockwise direction is increasing in magnitude and the rotational acceleration is negative is more difficult for students. To help with this difficulty, we use rotational motion diagrams. Students can use ActivPhysics simulations (available in MasteringPhysics) to help visualize the quantities and their signs.

Note that students are not accustomed to radians as a measure of angles; you will need to provide them with additional help as they work through the subsection on the units of rotational position in Section 8.1. It is useful to ask students to draw a one-radian angle on graph paper so they can clearly see that the arc length for one radian is equal to the radius of the circle. Another important idea in this section is the relationship between rotational and translational quantities. We have found a very powerful experiment to investigate this relationship: have one student hold the end of a stick that is several meters long. Have other students hold it at different distances from the end. Now have the student holding the end slowly turn in place. Everyone can see the outer students running while the inner students are walking slowly.

After students feel comfortable with the qualitative analysis of the kinematics of rotational motion, they are ready to move into a simplified description of the rotational motion at constant acceleration. Table 8.1 is very important; it helps students make an analogy that connects new ideas about rotational motion to their existing understanding of linear motion. For practice, use end-of-chapter problems 3, 4, 5, 6, 9, and 17.

II. Develop the Rotational Analog of Newton's Second Law

It is difficult (but not impossible) to derive a quantitative form of Newton's second law for rotational motion from observational experiments. Likewise, a full mathematical understanding of rotational dynamics is beyond the scope of an introductory algebra-based physics course. Therefore, we have decided to develop the rotational analog of Newton's second law as follows: Students start with *qualitative* observational and testing experiments that help them to build a conceptual understanding of the factors that affect the angular acceleration of an object (namely, the net torque exerted on the object, and the mass and mass distribution of the object). Then in textbook Section 8.4 and Active Learning Guide (ALG) activity 8.3.1, students can derive an equation for the rotational acceleration of a small block attached to a light stick that can move on a smooth surface in a circular path, having a force $\vec{F}$ exerted on it tangentially to the circle.

ALG activities 8.1.1 and 8.1.2 and textbook Observational Experiment Table 8.2 in Section 8.2 describe the experiments that help students devise qualitative patterns relating the torques produced by external forces exerted on a rigid body and the body's resulting rotational acceleration (the fourth experiment is especially important to help students establish the connection between the direction of the net torque and the resulting rotational acceleration). You can use a bicycle tire to perform the experiments in a lecture, or students can do them in a lab. It is very important here that they can clearly see the rotating tire and analyze the *changes* in its rotation. As students often confuse force and torque, Testing Experiment Table 8.3 helps them test two hypotheses: the rotational acceleration depends on the net force exerted on the object, or the rotational acceleration depends on the net torque produced by those forces. They find that the rotational acceleration depends on the net torque. Several ALG activities can be done in labs and in problem-solving recitations to help students become comfortable with finding net torque and understanding its relationship to rotational acceleration. These are ALG activities 8.1.3, 8.2.1, and 8.2.2.

Similar to how the sum of the forces exerted on a point-like object and its mass determine the object's resulting translational acceleration, the net torque produced by exerted forces along with the mass of the rigid body should determine the rotational acceleration of the rigid body. Students can investigate the effects of the body's mass distribution by working though textbook Section 8.3 and by doing ALG activities 8.1.4 and 8.1.5. We consider both discrete and continuous mass distributions. ALG activities and the Observational Experiment Table 8.4 help students construct the physical quantity of rotational inertia. Question 3 and problems 28 and 29 are also useful, as well as ALG activity 8.1.5.

ALG activity 8.3.1 and textbook Section 8.4 help students reason to the rotational form of Newton's second law for a simple case of a point-like object moving in a circle at the end of a massless rigid rod:

$$\alpha = \tau / mr^2$$

In this case, only one external object exerts a force on the circling object, and τ is the torque produced by that force. The above can be generalized for the case of multiple torques exerted on the object and for extended bodies with rotational inertia I:

$$\alpha = \Sigma\tau / I$$

This generalization cannot be done rigorously without calculus. The second half of Section 8.4 presents a heuristic approach by adding up contributions of several point objects to the overall moment of inertia of a rigid body. After students come up with the rotational form of Newton's second law, it is useful to emphasize the similarity between the mathematical descriptions of translational and rotational dynamics again (Table 8.5). If you wish, you can ask the students to fill out the table before they see it in the book and then consult with the book. To help students develop facility with the law, use ALG activity 8.3.3, all problems in ALG Section 8.4, and end-of-chapter problems 18, 20, 21, 22, 23, 24, 26, 27, 31, and 34.

Students encounter several difficulties with this material:

1. *The magnitude of the force that a string wrapped around a rotating disc exerts on an object of mass m hanging at the other end.* Often students think that the magnitude of the force that the string exerts on the disc is mg. Because the hanging object almost certainly accelerates, the magnitude of the force that the string exerts on the disc cannot equal the magnitude of the gravitational force that Earth exerts on the hanging object.
2. *Multi-object systems.* If a problem involves a rotating disc and one or more objects hanging from strings that pass around the disc, it is more productive if students choose those objects as separate systems for analysis and draw separate force diagrams for each object, including coordinate axes. It is easiest if the axes are oriented so that a positive (or negative) rotational acceleration for the disc produces a positive (or negative) linear acceleration for each of the hanging objects. This technique is used in the Atwood machine example (Example 8.6).
3. *Any problem* (such as Example 8.6) *that involves one or more objects hanging from a rotating flywheel.* Such a problem requires students to make the connection between the linear acceleration of the hanging object(s) and the

rotational acceleration of the flywheel. This is a very challenging conceptual hurdle for students and requires special attention from instructors.

Problems involving a rotating extended body attached to one or more hanging point objects take considerable time to solve and are probably not good problems for tests—especially multiple-choice tests. You could instead show a process in a sketch and ask students to choose the best force diagram for one or more of the objects shown in the sketch. For example, if a point object hangs from a string that wraps around a disc and the point object is moving down at increasing speed, you could ask students to choose the best of three force diagrams with different tension forces relative to the Earth's force exerted on the hanging object. For hand-graded problems, you could ask students to draw a force diagram for the hanging object, then make sure the forces have the correct relative magnitudes.

III. Develop the Ideas of Rotational Momentum and Rotational Kinetic Energy

Section 8.5 helps students construct a new physical quantity, rotational momentum. Although the observational experiments described in Table 8.7 are qualitative, they help establish a rule relating the changes in rotational velocity and rotational inertia of a spinning object:

> For an isolated extended body, when its rotational inertia I decreases, its rotational speed ω increases, and vice versa.

Students learn how to test the rule in Table 8.8 by predicting what will happen to the rotational velocity of a puck rotating in a circle at the end of a string as the string winds around the post to which it is attached. The reasoning is based on the rule formulated on the basis of Table 8.7: the rotational inertia $(I = mr^2)$ decreases and the magnitude of its rotational velocity increases. These experiments lead to the construction of the physical quantity rotational inertia using analogical reasoning: I is the rotational analog of the mass m of a point-like object and ω is the rotational analog of the object's translational velocity $\vec{v}$. Thus it is reasonable to propose a new quantity—rotational momentum L of a turning object (analogous to linear momentum $\vec{p} = m\vec{v}$)—that should be equal to $L = I\omega$. The analogy between the impulse-momentum equation and corresponding rotational quantities, in addition to the findings in Table 8.7 and 8.8, leads to a general rotational impulse-rotational momentum principle. The students then apply the principle quantitatively to a puck rotating in a circle, a record-breaking ice skater spin, and the spin-up of a pulsar as its size decreases. Students can apply and practice the concept by working on end-of-chapter questions 7, 10, and 12 and end-of-chapter problems 43, 45, and 47.

Section 8.6 helps students construct the expression for rotational kinetic energy. They test this expression in Testing Experiment Table 8.9 by using the expression to predict the outcome of a race down an incline of a solid disk and a hollow hoop, both of the same mass and radius. They later read about how to use the expression for rotational kinetic energy to analyze an ice skater spin and rotating discs (flywheels) used for energy storage. End-of-chapter problems 50, 52, 55, and 57 help students practice rotational kinetic energy ideas. A classic experiment with two bottles of the same mass, one filled with water and another filled with snow, rolling down an inclined plane helps students understand the difference between rolling and sliding. (Note that the water does not rotate with the rotating bottle that it is in; thus it only undergoes translational motion.) The experiment is easy to perform in class. In any case, treat this experiment as a testing experiment—have the students use their understanding of rotational motion to predict the outcome, then observe the experiment and have them revise their reasoning, if necessary. This is a good activity with which to use the think-pair-share technique. After you ask the questions, let students think quietly for 1 to 2 minutes (think), then turn to their neighbors to discuss their answers and come to a consensus (pair), and finally report the results of that consensus to the rest of the class (share).

IV. The Techniques and Skills Needed to Apply Rotational Motion Concepts to Interesting Everyday Examples

Section 8.7 uses ideas developed in the chapter to analyze two complex problems: (1) the effect of Earth's tides on the rotational speed of Earth, and therefore on the length of its day; and (2) the force that a cricket bowler's hand must exert on the ball while it is being bowled. The first example is important not only because it applies to what students have just learned (changing of the rotational velocity of Earth) but also because it gives students an opportunity to learn about tides and to go back to Chapter 4, where they learned the law of universal gravitation. Good problems for recitations are problems 39, 72, or 73. Corresponding ALG activities are in Section 8.4.

9

Gases

This is the first chapter that focuses on the properties of matter—in this case, primarily on gases. The next two chapters concern static and dynamic fluid phenomena (primarily liquids but a little on gases as well). We have broken the chapter into four parts:

I. *A qualitative analysis of the structure of matter*
II. *Development of the physical quantities pressure, density, and mass of a gas particle, and the development of the kinetic theory ideal gas model*
III. *Temperature and the development and testing of the ideal gas law*
IV. *Skills needed to analyze gas processes, including some real-world examples*
For each part, we provide examples of activities that can be used in the classroom and brief discussions of anticipated student difficulties with the subject matter.

Chapter subject matter	Related textbook section	ALG activities	End-of-chapter questions and problems	Videos
A qualitative analysis of the structure of matter	9.1	9.1.1–9.1.5	Questions 1, 5, 9, 10	9.1
Development of the physical quantities pressure, density, the mass of a gas particle, and the development of	9.2, 9.3	9.1.6–9.1.9, 9.2, 9.3.1–9.3.3	Problems 11, 12, 14, 17	

the kinetic theory ideal gas model				
Temperature and the development and testing of the ideal gas law	9.3–9.6	9.3.4–9.3.8	Questions 9–12, 15 Problems 24, 25, 29, 30, 33, 38, 44, 46, 53, 54, 58	9.3
Skills needed to analyze gas processes including some real-world examples	9.8, 9.9	9.4.1–9.4.6, 9.4.11–9.4.13	Problems 43, 45, 62, 69, 72	

We follow a "from microscopic to macroscopic" approach to the kinetic molecular theory (KMT) of gases. We start from the microscopic analysis of the behavior of gases. We devise the ideal gas model based on a few assumptions and Newton's laws and use it to derive the expression $PV = \frac{1}{3}Nm_{\text{particle}}v^2$. We then use experimental data to connect the average kinetic energy of particles to the temperature of the gas $\overline{K} = \frac{3}{2}kT$ and use this result to arrive at the canonical ideal gas law in the form $PV = nRT$. We finally test this equation by using it to predict the outcomes of real gas processes. In this approach, Boyle's and Charles's laws become the consequences of the microscopic gas analysis.

I. A Qualitative Analysis of the Structure of Matter

Students have learned about atoms and molecules throughout their earlier schooling. However, they are often unable to provide any evidence for the existence of atoms and molecules. Likewise, they have heard the word evaporation but have no idea what this word really means at the level of KMT. A set of activities in Section 9.1 of the Active Learning Guide (ALG) 9.1.1–9.1.5 and textbook Section 9.1 address these difficulties by engaging students in the analysis of an experiment in which they observe a streak of water or alcohol left on a paper by wiping a moist cotton ball across the paper. The streak slowly disappears from the edges, eventually vanishing entirely. If you decide to do these activities interactively in class, be careful with students' language. When you wipe alcohol on the board and ask the students what they see, they will invariably say "the alcohol is evaporating," without understanding what this really means. One strategy is to plead ignorance and ask them to describe what they see in nontechnical terms. Students should be able to come up with something like "the alcohol is disappearing gradually."

The goal of the ALG activities and the textbook section is to help students come up with an explanation for the gradual aspect of the disappearance and then suggest mechanisms that explain the disappearance itself. Here again, if you ask students to suggest mechanisms, they may say "evaporation." However, evaporation is not a mechanism; it is simply a technical term that gives a name to the phenomenon that they are studying. They then devise testing experiments to rule out one or more of these possible mechanisms (see the textbook Table 9.1). To do this, they need to think of experiments whose outcomes they can predict using each of these mechanisms, perform the experiments, and then compare the outcomes to the predictions. All of the experiments are easy to perform in class, so it is best if students go through this process by doing the ALG activities before they read Section 9.1. You can have these experiments prepared and ready to execute in class time.

Students might come up with mechanisms that are not mentioned in the section. In this case, you will need to help them think of new testing experiments. By the end of this process, usually there is only one possible mechanism that has not been disproved—that the liquid is made of small pieces (particles) that are in continual random motion. The section provides other experiments that can be explained using the same mechanism, such as Brownian motion. With all of this supporting evidence for an atomic model of matter (including explanations of macroscopic properties of different states of matter), students can then be introduced to the qualitative ideal gas model. You can use the textbook end-of-chapter question 1 and problems 5, 9, and 10 with students in recitations and lectures. While the qualitative analysis of the structure of matter may seem rather trivial for university students to engage in, it is a rare opportunity for students to practice the full cycle of scientific reasoning. (The cycle starts from observations, moves to developing multiple explanations, and then testing those explanations with the goal of eliminating some of them.) In our experience, students find the exercise highly enjoyable and rewarding.

II. Development of the Physical Quantities Pressure, Density, the Mass of a Gas Particle, and the Development of the Kinetic Theory Ideal Gas Model

The goal of ALG activities 9.1.6–9.1.8 and textbook Sections 9.2 and 9.3 is to help students develop an understanding of physical quantities that are necessary to describe gases macroscopically and microscopically as well as to devise a qualitative and quantitative microscopic explanation of pressure as the collisions of gas particles with the walls of the container.

A great way to begin this development is to start by blowing up a balloon in front of the class. Now that you have established that atoms and molecules are in a constant state of motion, students are quite comfortable with the idea that air molecules *inside* the balloon are bouncing off the walls of the balloon, pushing outward, and the more molecules you add, the more outward push there is (hence, the balloon inflates). Yet at the same time, many students think of air as empty space (we ourselves often speak of the air this way when we say, "Throw an object into the air."). Because of the way we talk about air, students often do not conceptualize air outside of the container as something that consists of moving particles that exert pressure on an object immersed in it. Thus, if you ask students what is stopping the balloon from expanding further (ALG activity 9.1.8), many will suggest that it is the rubber skin preventing further expansion (to add to the analysis, you might want to ask your students to choose an element of the balloon's skin and draw a force diagram for it after the balloon stops expanding). At this point, either a particularly sharp student or you, the instructor can introduce the alternate explanation that it is the air molecules outside of the balloon that are bombarding the walls of the balloon from the *outside*, preventing it from expanding further (again, a force diagram here is very helpful for analysis). Students can then test these two competing ideas using the experiment in Testing Experiment Table 9.2 (a balloon inside a vacuum jar), or ALG activity 9.1.9.

As an in-class activity you can ask students to make two predictions for the behavior of the balloon inside the vacuum jar, one for each explanation. Remember to remind students: A prediction is *not* a guess, it is a statement about what will happen if a particular explanation is true. It is important to differentiate between the physical quantity of pressure and the physical phenomenon of gas pressure that is explained by collisions of the particles with the walls of the container. Quantitative Exercise 9.1 emphasizes the concept that atmospheric air exerts pressure and uses the definition of pressure as a physical quantity to estimate the force exerted by the air against the front of a person's body.

After students have seen or done this calculation themselves, it is a great opportunity to demonstrate the huge force that atmospheric pressure can exert, for example, by inverting a graduated cylinder filled with water, covered on its open end by a flat (waterproof) piece of cardboard or plastic board. The physical quantity of density follows; students practice by estimating the density of a person's body in Quantitative Exercise 9.2 (material related to density is revisited again in Chapter 10 in relationship to floating and sinking). Finally, Avogadro's number, atomic mass, and the mole are introduced toward the end of Section 9.2 and used in Example 9.3 to estimate the average distance between air particles (about 30 times the diameter of an air particle). This exercise is extremely important, as it suggests the ideal gas model could be used to describe atmospheric air and also because it continues the theme of helping students learn how to do estimations. Activities in ALG section 9.2 (except 9.2.1) supplement Section 9.2 of the textbook.

ALG activities 9.2.1 and 9.3.1–9.3.3 and textbook Section 9.3 help students develop the quantitative aspect of the ideal gas model. It is important that students connect the derivation of the $PV = 1/3\ Nm_{\text{particle}}\overline{v^2}$ to their previous knowledge of momentum. Encourage them to use impulse-momentum bar charts when they derive the expression for the force that the wall exerts on a particle hitting it (ALG activity 9.3.2). It is also important to examine the equation after students derive it (ALG activity 9.3.3). For example, doubling the number of the particles inside the container doubles the gas pressure, but doubling the root-mean-squared (rms) speed leads to the increase of the pressure by 4 times. Rewriting the above equation as

$$PV = \frac{2}{3}N\left(\frac{1}{2}m\overline{v^2}\right) = \frac{2}{3}N\overline{K}$$

helps students establish the connection between pressure and the average kinetic energy of particles:

$$PV = \frac{2}{3}N\left(\frac{1}{2}m\overline{v^2}\right) = \frac{2}{3}N\overline{K}$$

Students can now use this equation to estimate the average root-mean-square speed of air particles (textbook Example 9.4). When they calculate the result, it is important to stop and ask whether this result seems to make sense. If the speed of the particles is so high, why does the smell of perfume from an open bottle take minutes to spread from one corner of a room to the other? In general, it is useful to establish a rule that students must evaluate every new equation that is derived in the book by looking at limiting cases and seeing that it is consistent with the rest of their physics knowledge.

End-of-chapter problems 11, 12, 14, and 17 help students develop student facility in using these ideas. We hope that by the end of these sections, students have developed a robust physical intuition for what a gas is really like on a microscopic level: the speed of the gas molecules, the amount of space between them, and the fact that a gas exerts a large amount of force on the walls of its container due to the collective action of a vast number (10^{23}) of individual molecules.

III. Temperature and the Development and Testing of the Ideal Gas Law

In Section 9.3, students derived the relation between the pressure exerted by the gas particles on the wall of a container and their average kinetic energy. From experience, students know there is a connection between the temperature of a gas and its pressure. How then does temperature enter into the above-mentioned relation? After students review Celsius and Fahrenheit scales, they learn how to establish the connection between pressure and temperature through constructing a new temperature scale. This process is based on the observation that PV/N is a constant for any two gases in thermal equilibrium with each other, and that PV/N increases with the temperature (in Celsius) of the gas. Using proportional reasoning and some provided data, students arrive at the relation between the quantities used to describe gases:

$$\frac{PV}{N} = kT$$

where T is the temperature measured on the kelvin scale. As students know from Section 9.3 that $PV = 2/3\ N\overline{K}$, they can establish the connection between the new temperature and the average kinetic energy of particles $\overline{K} = 3/2\ kT$. After students calculate the value of the proportionality constant, they can develop another form of the ideal gas law by rewriting N in terms of the number of moles n of gas:

$$PV = nRT$$

In class, you can either follow ALG activities 9.3.4–9.3.8 or the discussion described in textbook Section 9.4 to connect $PV = 2/3\ N\overline{K}$ to the temperature of the gas. Textbook Section 9.5 outlines the steps that students might take to test the gas law $(PV = nRT)$. by predicting what will happen to a constant mass of gas if one of the macroscopic physical quantities is held constant while a second one changes. They do it for three different pairs of variables in Table 9.5 (encourage students to work through the steps outlined in the table before actually reading the text), eventually arriving at the mathematical descriptions and experimental tests of various iso-processes. Table 9.6 summarizes the processes. Students then work through the problems that apply those ideas to breathing and to what happens to a half-filled water bottle carried by a passenger on an airplane flight.

The speed distribution of gas particles is the subject of Section 9.6. We do not derive Maxwell's distribution, but we show how it was experimentally tested by Stern. The last paragraph of this section summarizes the process by which students constructed their new knowledge of the behavior of gases.

Students can apply the concepts in Sections 9.3–9.6 in lectures or in recitations with end-of-chapter questions 9, 10, 11, 12, and 15 and end-of-chapter problems 24, 25, 29, 30, 33, 38, 44, 46, 53, 54, and 58.

IV. Skills Needed to Analyze Gas Processes, Including Some Real-World Examples

Section 9.4 of the ALG helps students master graphical representations of gas processes that allow them to connect macroscopic descriptions to microscopic explanations. Use ALG activities 9.4.1–9.4.5 before you move to textbook Example 9.8 in Section 9.8, which provides the techniques that students can use to adapt the general problem-solving procedure to gas law problems (the example involves the size of a scuba diver's lungs as he or she rises to the surface). This example can be followed by ALG activities 9.4.6–9.4.11 and 9.4.13. Other examples in this section and in Section 9.9 involve the thermal energy of air in an empty cup (enough to lift the air 14,000 m above Earth's surface), the time interval the Sun would shine if it depended only on its current thermal energy, and the diffusion of O_2 from the capillaries to body cells. You could ask students in recitations to work on the more complex problems 43, 45, 62, 69, and 72. A possible lab experiment is described in ALG activity 9.4.12. Students will return to the concepts of temperature, thermal energy, and energy transfer in Chapters 12 and 13 when they study thermodynamics.

10

Static Fluids

In Chapter 9, we constructed the ideal gas model and used it to explain the behavior of gases. The next two chapters concern static and dynamic fluids phenomena (primarily liquids but a little on gases as well). We have broken this static fluids chapter into four parts:

I. *Density*. In Section 10.1, students are reintroduced to the mathematical concept of density and also summarize a pattern that they already probably know about the relationship between density and sinking or floating. Instead of trying to explain this pattern straight away, we put it aside and return to explain this pattern at the beginning of Section 10.7, only *after* students have developed a complete understanding of buoyant force.

II. *Students develop the concepts of pressure variation in a fluid and the dependence of pressure on the depth in the fluid* (Sections 10.2–10.4).

III. *Buoyant force*. In Section 10.5, students start with an observational experiment that allows them to observe patterns related to the buoyant force that a fluid exerts on an object floating or immersed in it. They then proceed directly to develop a mathematical explanation for the buoyant force using Pascal's second law. Finally, they interpret the mathematical model physically as Archimedes' principle. Section 10.6 develops students' understanding of buoyant force through simple applications.

IV. *Consider many interesting examples of fluid statics in the real world.* In Section 10.7, students have a chance to put it all together: First we connect back to Section 10.1 and formalize the relationship between densities and floating and sinking in a fluid. Then students can learn about ship design and stability, ballooning, altitude sickness, scuba diving, and decompression sickness.

Chapter subject matter	Related textbook section	ALG activities	End-of-chapter questions and problems	Videos
Density	10.1	10.3.1	Question 5 Problems 4–6, 9, 11	
Develop the concepts of pressure variation in a fluid and the dependence of pressure on the depth in the fluid	10.2–10.4	10.1.1–10.1.3, 10.2.2, 10.2.3, 10.3.2–10.3.4	Questions 2, 6, 10–12 Problems 20, 21, 23–25, 32–34, 36, 37, 42, 50, 85, 86	
Derive an expression for the buoyant force that a fluid exerts on an object in the fluid and learn to apply this and other fluid concepts to problem solving	10.5, 10.6	10.1.5, 10.1.6, 10.3.5–10.3.10, 10.4.4–10.4.9	Questions 7, 9, 13, 15, 18 Problems 55, 57, 60, 62, 63, 64, 74, 87, 90	10.4
Interesting real-world examples of fluid statics	10.7		Questions 16, 17, 19, 20 Problems 75, 78, 84	

I. Density

Students learned about density in Chapter 9. However, the concept of density as the slope of the mass versus volume graph is difficult for the students, and thus we recommend that you help them by doing Active Learning Guide (ALG) activity 10.3.1 (there is no parallel table in the textbook). In this chapter, students connect an object's density with its ability to float or sink in a fluid. While most students have probably already learned this idea in a middle school science class, we offer a more novel example of a helium balloon immersed in air. Students may not have considered this example in the same category as wooden and metal blocks, respectively, floating and sinking in a beaker of water. It is probably a good idea to draw their attention to this. An interesting example involves the lower density of ice relative to water and its effect on the ability of fish and plants to survive winter freezes in ponds and lakes. You can follow up with end-of-chapter question 5 and problems 4, 5, 6, 9, and 11.

II. Develop the Concepts of Pressure Variation in a Fluid and the Dependence of Pressure on the Depth in the Fluid

The goal of Part II is for students to develop, test, and apply two related ideas about the behavior of pressure in fluids: Pascal's first and second laws. The key ideas that students have to develop for Pascal's first law are that (1) a fluid exerts pressure in all directions (ALG activity 10.1.1) and (2) that a change in pressure is redistributed equally throughout the fluid (textbook Section 10.2, particularly Figures 10.4a and b). For Pascal's second law, students need to realize that pressure increases with depth and to develop a "layer" model. In this model, we break up the fluid into layers and choose one layer of a fluid as a system. As each layer of the fluid is in the state of static equilibrium, the forces exerted on it from all directions should cancel each other. In the downward direction two objects exert forces on the layer—all of the layers pushing from above and Earth. In the upward direction, it is only the fluid that exerts a force. Therefore, if we compare two layers inside the fluid, one closer to the top and the other one closer to the bottom, the upward force exerted on the layer that is deeper in the fluid should be larger than the upward force exerted on the layer that is closer to the top. (ALG activities 10.1.2, 10.1.3, and 10.2.2 and textbook Section 10.3.)

We would like to point out that, because the two laws are so interrelated, there is more than one way for students to develop their ideas. The ALG asks students to develop both laws simultaneously in a qualitative form (ALG activities 10.1.1–10.1.3). However, in the textbook, students first develop Pascal's first law in Section 10.2. Then they immediately learn about applications of this idea, such as a hydraulic lift or press (ALG activity 10.2.3 is an accompanying activity for this). In the textbook, a second cycle begins in Section 10.3, where students test Pascal's first law by examining the pressure in a fluid at different depths. This is a case where the prediction from Pascal's first law (equal pressure throughout) is contradicted by the results of the experiment. Accordingly, students have to modify Pascal's first law to account for the pressure variance with depth. This is achieved by introducing the layer model. In contrast, the ALG uses data tables in activities 10.3.2 and 10.3.3 while the textbook uses analogical reasoning to derive Pascal's second law for layers of a liquid in a tube. The accompanying empirical or mathematical development results in Pascal's second law: $P_1 = P_2 + \rho_{\text{fluid}}(y_2 - y_1)g$. One difficulty that students face here is to recognize that the pressure of a fluid depends on its height above the level of interest, not the total mass of the fluid. ALG activity 10.3.4 helps students test both ideas.

Textbook Section 10.4 offers students a test and some applications of Pascal's second law. Students can use these laws to explain glaucoma and why our ears pop when we move to higher elevations (Example 10.4). Torricelli hypothesized that it is atmospheric air pressure exerted on the surface of water that pushes the water 10 meters up an evacuated tube. A test of this idea, described in Table 10.3, was performed with an evacuated tube in mercury. This led to a method to measure pressure. Students learn how to apply this idea to a diving bell lowered into water in Example 10.5. End-of-chapter questions and problems that can be used with students in lectures and recitations to help develop student understanding and facility in using these ideas in problem solving include: for Section 10.2, question 2 and problems 20, 21, 23, 24, 25; for Section 10.3, question 6 and problems 32, 33, 34, 36, 37, 42, and 86; and for Section 10.4, questions 10, 11, and 12 and problems 50 and 85.

III. Derive an Expression for the Buoyant Force that a Fluid Exerts on an Object in the Fluid and Learn to Apply This and Other Fluid Concepts to Problem Solving

Many students hold an idea that air pushes down on objects. ALG activities 10.1.5 and 10.1.6 help students develop and test the concept that the net force exerted by a fluid on a submerged object points up. Quantitative development for the quantity of the buoyant force is described in Table 10.4 on page 372, where a solid block is lowered slowly into water by a string that is suspended at the other end to a spring scale, and in ALG activities 10.3.5–10.3.7. The scale reading decreases as the block becomes more submerged and is then constant after the block is completely submerged but lowered even deeper in the fluid.

Students need to carefully examine the data and find the patterns to decide how the net force that the liquid exerts on the submerged object depends on various physical quantities. Notice that in ALG activity 10.3.5 there are two objects of different density (students have to deduce this), which allows the students to devise the patterns and to see that the force that fluid exerts on the submerged object does not depend on the mass of the object but on the submerged volume. There are two ways that you could approach the development of the buoyant force. The data from the observational experiments is sufficient to develop the relationship empirically.

In the textbook, we present an alternate method where the buoyant force relationship is derived from Pascal's second law and then given physical meaning as Archimedes' principle. Tips for using the principle to determine the magnitude of the upward buoyant force that a fluid exerts on a partially or totally submerged object appear at the end of Section 10.5. It is important to remind students that the density in the expression for the buoyant force is the density of the fluid and not of the object in the fluid. The biggest difficulty here is to recognize that the buoyant force does not change after the object is totally submerged (notice the last readings for both blocks in ALG activity 10.3.5). ALG activities 10.3.8–10.3.10 help students test and solidify their ideas. This is the subtle part of the pattern that students have to observe, and you may need to draw their attention to it.

The strategy for problem solving is adapted to the analysis of static fluid processes in Example 10.6 in Section 10.6. Example 10.7 illustrates it for the problem where it is necessary to determine the density of the metal in a crown—the famous Archimedes' problem. The concepts in Sections 10.5 and 10.6 can be applied with students in lectures or in recitations to end-of-chapter questions 7, 9, 13, 15, and 18 and end-of-chapter problems 55, 57, 60, 62, 63, 64, 74, 87, and 90. ALG activities 10.4.4–10.4.7 provide examples of the problems developing high-order thinking skills, and ALG activities 10.4.8 and 10.4.9 are examples of the labs that the students can do after they are comfortable with Archimedes' principle.

IV. Consider Many Interesting Examples of Fluid Statics in the Real World

Section 10.7 begins by revisiting the well-known empirical rule that if an object is less dense than the fluid it is immersed in, it will float, whereas if it is more dense than the fluid, it will sink. Section 10.7 also has many interesting real-world problems that involve buoyancy and other fluid statics phenomena:

- How submarines sink and rise in the water
- The conditions needed for ships to be stable
- The number of people a life raft can hold
- Ballooning
- Scuba diving and breathing methods as the diver descends, so external and internal pressures balance
- Oxygen overload during scuba diving
- Decompression sickness when ascend during a dive

You could ask students in recitations to work on questions 16, 17, 19, and 20 and problems 75, 78, and 84.

11

Fluids in Motion

In Chapter 10, we developed ideas about the pressure in static fluids and how pressure variation leads to an upward buoyant force that the fluid exerts on an object that is partially or totally submerged in the fluid. In this chapter, we consider two new effects: the effect of moving fluids on the surface or wall of a tube across which the fluid moves and the effect of a fluid on an object that moves through the fluid. We have broken this chapter into three parts:

I. *A qualitative introduction to Bernoulli's principle, and ideas concerning flow rate and types of fluid flow*
II. *A quantitative development of Bernoulli's equation and the skills and applications for applying it quantitatively*
III. *Viscous fluid flow and drag forces*

For each part, we provide examples of activities that can be used in the classroom and brief discussions of motivation for those activities and anticipated student difficulties with the subject matter.

Chapter subject matter	**Related textbook section**	**ALG activities**	**End-of-chapter questions and problems**	**Videos**
A qualitative introduction to Bernoulli's principle, and ideas concerning flow rate and types of fluid flow	11.1–11.3	11.1.1–11.1.6, 11.2.1–11.2.3, 11.3.1	Questions 1–8, 12 Problems 2, 3, 5	11.1, 11.2

A quantitative development of Bernoulli's equation and the skills and applications for applying it quantitatively	11.4, 11.5, 11.7	11.3.2, 11.4.2–11.4.8	Problems 7–16, 19, 22, 23, 31, 33, 35	
Viscous fluid flow and drag forces	11.6, 11.8		Problems 27, 28, 30, 39, 41, 42, 53, 57	

I. A Qualitative Introduction to Bernoulli's Principle, and Ideas Concerning Flow Rate and Types of Fluid Flow

There are many simple and fun experiments that students can use to find a pattern in the relationship between the speed of a moving fluid and the pressure that it exerts on a surface that it moves across. Remember, let students first observe the phenomena without predicting! Their natural surprise is the opportunity for them to try and explain why the phenomena are happening.

If you start this chapter in lecture, follow the sequence from Section 11.1 in the textbook. If you start in a lab, students can perform activities 11.1.1–11.1.4 in the Active Learning Guide (ALG) to come up with a qualitative version of the Bernoulli principle. Table 11.1 in Section 11.1 describes a series of observational experiments. Notice that this table provides two explanations of the observed phenomena (these are the two most common explanations that students devise). Ask your students to come up with ways to test those explanations, or ask them to use the two explanations to make predictions for the outcomes of testing experiments described in the textbook's Table 11.2.

This is a good opportunity to remind students that each of their predictions should be based on whichever explanation is being tested. The explanation that is not rejected is provisionally accepted and stated in a qualitative form as Bernoulli's principle, which students then apply to explain how a clarinet reed works and why people snore. This progression is a self-contained cycle: conducting observational experiments, inferring patterns, constructing explanations, designing testing experiments, making predictions of their outcomes using constructed explanations, conducting testing experiments, comparing outcomes to the predictions, and making judgments about the explanations. You can use ALG activities 11.2.1 and 11.2.2 and questions 1–7 and 12 as additional tests and applications of this qualitative hypothesis.

The next step is the concept of flow rate. The textbook provides an operational definition for the flow rate (Equation 11.1) and then proceeds to the derivation of what affects the flow rate—average speed v through a tube or vessel of cross-sectional area A (Equation 11.2). Matching ALG activities are 11.1.5, 11.1.6, and 11.3.1. If the vessel is rigid and changes dimensions at one part compared to another, we get the continuity equation. You can use question 8 and problems 2, 3, and 5 in recitations and lectures. Section 11.3 introduces students to laminar-streamline and turbulent flow and helps contrast the two.

We recommend that you use an activity like ALG activity 11.2.3 either for an interactive class discussion with clicker responses or for discussion in recitation. Students can be separately comfortable with the qualitative form of Bernoulli's principle and the continuity equation for incompressible fluids. However, when asked to put both ideas together to explain what is going on in an activity like ALG activity 11.2.3, they are likely to be confused. Students struggle with the intuitive idea that if a space is "constricted" (the narrowing pipe) the pressure should be higher. Letting students talk to each other while trying to explain ALG activity 11.2.3 (with an accompanying live demo, if you have it) can help students to work through their difficulties with this rather counterintuitive result. You can help students think about this problem by encouraging them to compare the speed of the fluid at two different points. Asking them to think about what causes the fluid to speed up should lead them to think about the need for a difference in pressure between two points. For the fluid to accelerate, the pressure would need to be higher in the region where the fluid is moving slower as compared to the region where it is moving faster. Having students think about the pressure difference naturally focuses their thinking for the next section, where they have to derive the complete quantitative form of Bernoulli's equation.

II. A Quantitative Development of Bernoulli's Equation and the Skills and Applications for Applying It Quantitatively

Textbook Section 11.4 and ALG activity 11.3.2 lead students through the derivation of the Bernoulli equation using the work-energy principle. Following the derivation, it would be good to show how the math is consistent with the outcomes of the experiments in Tables 11.1 and 11.2. If you feel that your students are not motivated by derivations, you can show them the concepts behind the derivation using Bernoulli bar charts—the fluid analog of a work-energy bar chart. Bernoulli bar charts have the same underlying idea as work-energy bar charts, except they use energy density instead of energy, and pressure difference instead of work. They provide an insightful way to analyze a fluid-dynamic process and help students make a conceptual bridge from the physical system to the mathematical representation. Consider the following form of Bernoulli's equation that represents the energy conservation for a unit volume of fluid:

$$\frac{1}{2}\rho v_1^{\ 2} + \rho g y_1 + (P_1 - P_2) = +\frac{1}{2}\rho v_2^{\ 2} + \rho g y_2$$

Here is how this equation can be reconceptualized using a bar chart: A system, consisting of a unit volume of fluid and Earth, has kinetic and potential energy densities that change when the system is subjected to a pressure variation. We can represent the process using bars for kinetic energy density $1/2\rho v$, gravitational potential energy density $\rho g y$ for the two states, and pressure difference $P_1 - P_2$. Once students construct a bar chart for a process, they can use it to help them apply the Bernoulli equation to the process.

Example 11.3 in Section 11.5 shows students how to analyze fluid dynamics processes quantitatively. There are several key strategies to emphasize. First, Bernoulli's equation is applied to two different positions or points in a moving fluid. It is important to have a sketch of the process and to have the points clearly identified. Second, one point is chosen in order to determine some unknown quantity needed to solve the problem (for example, the pressure at the output of a pump). The second point is chosen at a place where everything about the moving fluid is known. Third, to specify the gravitational potential energy density, the student must specify a vertical *y*-axis and choose an origin or zero point, just as they did for gravitational potential energy. Fourth, when constructing a qualitative Bernoulli bar chart, it is often easiest to make the gravitational energy density bars first, then the kinetic energy bars, and finally the pressure bars, so that the sum of the three terms at position 1 equals the sum at position 2. Remember that the bar heights are qualitative and unknown exactly. The pressure bars are adjusted to make the three terms on the left side of the chart equal to the three on the right side. Also, note that the pressure bars are due to external agents and are placed in a shaded region (like the work bars when doing work-energy processes). ALG activities 11.4.2–11.4.5 and end-of-chapter problems 7–15 help students practice moving from the sketches of the physical processes to bar charts to equations and from equations to bar charts and sketches of the processes.

Section 11.7 shows students how to apply Bernoulli's equation to three interesting processes: a high-speed wind lifting the roof up off a house; the rapid flow of blood past a narrow, plaque-constricted region in a blood vessel, thus dislodging and lifting the plaque off the vessel wall; and measuring blood pressure. ALG activities 11.4.6–11.4.8 and end-of-chapter problems 16, 19, 22, 23, 31, 33, and 35 can be used in lectures and recitations to help develop student understanding and facility in problem solving.

You may notice the startling omission of applying Bernoulli's principle to an aircraft wing. This omission is deliberate. In modern aircraft design, the boundary layer of air in contact with the wing surface is normally turbulent, not laminar. Thus with very few exceptions (e.g., the Supermarine Spitfire and Lockheed SR-71 Blackbird), most modern aircraft do not rely on Bernoulli's principle to generate lift—a fact that an attentive student could point out by noting that many aircraft seem to perform just fine when flown upside-down.

III. Viscous Fluid Flow and Drag Forces

We believe that it is critically important for student motivation and interest that they see the physics they study as connected to their experience of everyday life. Thus we have devoted the final part to studying fluids in a more realistic setting where the effects of viscosity and friction are considered. Section 11.6 starts with a qualitative discussion of friction, leading to the idea of friction flow in fluids (viscous fluid flow). Four factors are identified that affect the flow rate through a tube or vessel with a viscous fluid flowing through it: (1) the pressure decrease from the input to the output of the vessel, (2) the radius of the vessel, (3) the length of the vessel, and (4) the type of fluid flowing characterized by the viscosity of the fluid. Table 11.3 provides data for analyzing how each quantity affects the flow rate. After such analysis, students will have an easier time understanding where Poiseuille's law, which determines the pressure decrease across a vessel needed for a particular flow rate, comes from. Notice the unit analysis that we use to determine the units for the viscosity. Quantitative Exercise 11.5 applies this idea to the analysis of the effect of flow rate and pressure drop across a narrow part of an artery with plaque. You may consider skipping this entire section, but there is a useful connection that could be made between Poiseuille's law and Ohm's law and the resistivity equation in DC circuits. Although the functional relationship is not the same, the qualitative relationship is similar (larger r, larger flow rate; larger l, lower flow rate). If you intend to use water-pipe analogies when covering DC circuits next semester, it could be extremely useful to have students work through the real-life subtleties of fluid flow now. They can then draw on that understanding when working with Ohm's law and the resistivity equation.

The drag force that a fluid exerts on an object moving through the fluid is examined in Section 11.8 for the cases of laminar flow and turbulent flow (both equations are given without derivation or backup data—a rare case in this textbook). The latter idea is applied to the drag force that air exerts on a car (Example 11.8) and the terminal speed of a skydiver (Example 11.9). Because both drag force equations (Equations 11.10 and 11.12) contain several new symbols, it is important to ask the students to explain what each term means and to describe what they imagine when they see each equation. It is easier to do it first in the context of a particular problem, and then ask students to describe a situation for which a particular equation might be relevant. End-of-chapter problems 27, 28, 30, 39, 41, 42, 53, and 57 serve as good applications for the concepts in Sections 11.6–11.8.

12

First Law of Thermodynamics

In Chapters 10 and 11, we developed ideas about static and dynamic fluids. The focus was on the physical quantities force and pressure and the microscopic mechanisms that explain processes in the fluids. In this chapter, we bring the energy approach into the analysis, and we add a new mechanism through which the energy of a system can change—heating. Before, students only knew work as a mechanism of energy transfer. We also help them connect the microscopic understanding of the gas processes to the work-heating-energy concepts.

We have broken this first chapter on thermodynamics into four parts:

I. *Define the work done on a gas, the internal energy of a gas, heating, and the first law of thermodynamics*
II. *Develop the ideas of temperature change and state changes*
III. *Apply the first law of thermodynamics to gas processes (so-called iso-processes)*
IV. *Apply the knowledge of heating mechanisms and the first law of thermodynamics to real-life phenomena*

For each part, we provide examples of activities that can be used in the classroom and brief discussions of anticipated student difficulties with the subject matter.

Chapter subject matter	Related textbook section	ALG activities	End-of-chapter questions and problems	Videos
Define the work done on a gas, energy provided	12.1–12.3	12.1.1–12.1.5, 12.2.1, 12.2.2	Questions 1, 4 Problems 5, 6	12.1

through heating to the gas, the internal energy of a gas, and the first law of thermodynamics				
Develop the ideas of temperature change and state changes	12.4, 12.6	12.3.1–12.3.5, 12.4.2–12.4.10	Questions 6–9 Problems 7, 8, 10, 12, 16, 18, 31, 34, 38, 40, 42	12.4
Apply the first law of thermodynamics to gas processes (so-called iso-processes)	12.5	12.4.1, 12.4.11–12.4.13	Question 5 Problems 20, 21, 24, 30	
Apply the knowledge of heating mechanisms and the first law of thermodynamics to real-life phenomena	12.7, 12.8		Question 10 Problems 46, 49, 50, 52, 55, 60, 62	

There are a few ideas that make our approach different from the traditional approach:

1. We continue to use the system approach—the system has energy, and this energy can be changed through two mechanisms: work and heating. The mechanism of work explains the energy transfer when there is mechanical motion of some parts of the system or volume change due to the interaction with the environment. The mechanism of heating explains the energy transfer when the system and the environment are at different temperatures and no work is done.
2. We do not use the term heat for the mechanism of energy transfer because students often think that heat is something that belongs to the system. We use the word heating instead.
3. We add space for the heating bar on the energy bar chart next to the space for work so that it becomes the work-heating-energy bar chart, showing that all energy is transferred to the system from the environment through work and heating (the energy can be positive or negative).

We only have one statement for the first law of thermodynamics: $W_{\text{Environment on System}} + Q_{\text{Environment to System}} = \Delta U_{\text{System}}$

I. Define the Work Done on a Gas, Energy Provided through Heating to the Gas, the Internal Energy of a Gas, and the First Law of Thermodynamics

In Section 12.1, students learn how to apply the definition of mechanical work done by an external force on a point-like object as the object moves to derive the expression for the work done by a piston on the gas in a cylinder (the gas is the system) as the gas volume changes:

$$W_{\text{Piston on Gas}} = -F_{\text{P on G}}\Delta x = -(P \cdot A)\left(\frac{\Delta V}{A}\right) = -P\Delta V$$

Notice the minus sign here. When the volume of the gas decreases, the environment does positive work on the system, and when the volume of the gas increases, the environment does negative work. It is important to emphasize here that work is not a state variable but instead depends on the particular way that the gas takes to move from the initial state to the final state of the gas; the work done by the environment on a gas $W_{\text{Environment on gas}}$ is the negative of the area under the P-vs-V graph for that process. In Section 9.4, this property of work is contrasted with the thermal energy of a gas. Thermal energy is a **state function**, which depends only on the temperature of the gas

$$U_{\text{thermal}} = N\left(\frac{3}{2}kT_{\text{K}}\right) = \frac{3}{2}nRT_{\text{K}}$$

when in a particular state. Note that the Active Learning Guide (ALG) does not have an activity parallel to the derivation of work expression.

You can lead the discussion by using Table 12.1 in Section 12.2, which describes energy transfer experiments. Correlational ALG activities 12.1.1–12.1.4 can help students devise and apply the new quantity that describes the process of transfer of energy to the system. Students realize that the work-energy principle they studied in Chapter 6 cannot explain the transfer of energy. They may feel that the principle is incorrect or that it needs modification—adding a new mechanism of energy transfer, which the students define as **heating.** Heating Q is a physical quantity that characterizes the amount of energy transferred from the environment to the system when they are at different temperatures. Students should understand that the word heating means a process through which the energy of a system changes, not some substance that resides in the system. In addition, they should understand that in some instances there can be energy transferred to the system through the process of heating, but the system does not "heat up"— the temperature does not change (or it might even go down).

After students define heating as the process of energy transfer, they can proceed to Observational Experiment Table 12.3 in Section 12.3, where they use the work-energy principle with heating added to explain the experiments performed in Table 12.1. ALG activities 12.1.3–12.1.5 correlate to the textbook section. This new principle succeeds in explaining many phenomena that the old work-energy principle could not—such as the change of the temperature of water (the system) placed on a hot electric stove (the environment), or the change in the temperature of a hot, hard-boiled egg (the system) placed in a bowl of cold water (the environment). The new principle is called the **first law of thermodynamics**, which is the extension of the work-energy principle to the thermodynamic processes. Use ALG activities 12.2.1 and 12.2.2 and end-of-chapter questions 1 and 4 and problems 5 and 6 in recitations and lectures to help students apply the first law of thermodynamics qualitatively. In all those examples work is done *on* the system and the energy is provided *to* the system through heating (both can be positive or negative). The system does not do work.

II. Develop the Ideas of Temperature Change and State Change

Activities in textbook Sections 12.4 and 12.6 and Section 12.3 of the ALG help students construct the physical quantities of specific heat and latent heat. The sequence in ALG activities 12.3.1–12.3.4 can be done in recitations or lectures to help students construct the quantity of specific heat before they do the lab (ALG activity 12.3.5). Note that we define the **specific heat** of a substance as the physical quantity equal to the amount of energy (and not heating) that needs to be added to 1 kilogram of the substance to increase its temperature by 1 °C. Often this energy is added through heating, but the temperature of a substance can change by doing work or by both processes. Thus we have $\Delta U = cm\Delta T$ instead of the traditional $Q = cm\Delta T$, an expression that promotes an unnecessary difficulty. Only when there is no work involved in the process can we say that $Q = cm\Delta T$.

While students work with solids and liquids and there is no change of state, the temperature changes when the system's energy is changed through heating. However, if a gas is involved or the material changes state, the heating might not lead to the temperature change. Thus it is important to discuss this nuance in language with students. Just as with the word "work," physics has recruited an everyday word and endowed it with a much more specialized meaning. In everyday life, the verb "heating" is equated with warming, but in physics this is not the case. In our experience, students need to be reminded of this fact more than once.

For example, when energy is provided through the mechanism of heating, it can lead to changes in state (Section 12.6)—melting and freezing or boiling and condensing. The energy in joules needed to melt a mass m of a solid at its melting temperature or the energy released when a mass m of the liquid freezes at that same temperature is:

$$\Delta U = \pm mL_f \tag{12.6}$$

L_f is the heat of fusion of the substance (see Table 12.7). The plus sign is used when the substance melts and the minus sign when it freezes. Note that the word heat of fusion is confusing, because in our common language heat is often associated with warming (i.e., temperature change). In the case of melting or freezing, there is no temperature change. However, there is still change in internal energy, the potential energy of interactions of the particles in the system. The same arguments apply to the heat of vaporization: the energy in joules ΔU needed to transform a mass m of a liquid at its boiling temperature into the gaseous state at the same temperature is

$$\Delta U = \pm mL_v \tag{12.7}$$

where L_v is the heat of vaporization of the substance. The plus sign is the energy needed to boil the liquid, and the minus sign is the energy released when the gas condenses.

ALG activities 12.4.2–12.4.8 show a sequence you can use in recitations, and activities 12.4.9 and 12.4.10 are ready lab activities. End-of-chapter questions 6–9 and problems 7, 8, 10, 12, 16, 18, 31, 34, 38, 40, and 42 can be used in lectures and homework.

III. Apply the First Law of Thermodynamics to Gas Processes (So-Called Iso-Processes)

Section 12.5 and ALG activities 12.4.1 and 12.4.11–12.4.13 help students combine the microscopic approach to the gas processes with the work-heating-energy approach. This builds their knowledge and helps them to recognize the fundamental differences between the concept of energy as a state function and the concepts of work and heating that are energy transfer *processes*. To help students learn these ideas, we encourage them to represent the processes using words, graphs, bar charts, and equations and to explain what happens using a microscopic approach (molecules and their motion) and a first law of thermodynamics approach (positive or negative energy transfer to the system and the changes in the system's energy).

Students have a difficult time understanding microscopically how the temperature of a gas can change due to work done on it by the environment. It helps if the students can visualize the change in the speed of a gas molecule when it hits a piston moving inward or outward (a contracting or expanding gas). (See the beginning of Section 12.5.)

The gas molecules move slightly slower after colliding with the expanding piston. As a result, the temperature of the gas decreases as the piston moves outward. The environment does negative work on the gas. Similarly, if the piston moves inward, the average speed of the particles after colliding with the piston will be greater than before the collision. In this case, the temperature of the gas increases as the piston moves inward and does positive work on the gas. We think it is worth letting students work through this analysis in some detail since it allows them to use the ideas of reference frames and conservation of momentum, two ideas they have already encountered in earlier work.

Understanding microscopically how a moving piston can change the temperature of a gas is important in analyzing so-called iso-processes that students first encountered in Chapter 9 using the first law of thermodynamics (see Table 12.6). The issue of work and heating not being state functions is addressed in ALG activity 12.4.1. This activity is based on research work that shows that even after instruction on the first law, students still think that when a system undergoes a process and it returns to the original state, all of the quantities of work, heating, and internal energy change are equal to zero. It is useful to have students work through ALG activity 12.4.1 in groups and resolve any discrepancies that they encounter through discussion with each other. The idea that the internal energy of the gas is a state function but heating and work are not is one of the most challenging ideas for students to figure out. Example 12.6 outlines the problem-solving strategy for using the first law of thermodynamics to analyze gas processes for a hot air balloon, and Example 12.7 applies it for the temperature control of a doomed stadium. Use end-of-chapter question 5 and problems 20, 21, 24, and 30 for more practice.

IV. Heating Mechanisms and Important Real-World Applications of the First Law Thermodynamics

Section 12.7 is dedicated to the discussion of specific mechanisms through which heating occurs (conduction, convection, radiation, and evaporation), and Section 12.8 applies these ideas to the greenhouse effect and climate control and for body temperature control (for example, while running a long distance on a hot, summer day). Here you can use end-of-chapter question 10 and problems 46, 49, 50, 52, 55, 60, and 62.

13

Second Law of Thermodynamics

In Chapter 12, students learned about the new method of energy transfer—heating—and how to include this method in the work-energy equation: the first law of thermodynamics. In this chapter, students find that many processes that are allowed by the first law of thermodynamics actually do not occur. This leads to the development of the second law of thermodynamics and a way to decide if an energy conversion process is possible. The chapter then applies the second law to analyze the efficiency of various practical devices like motors and refrigerators. This chapter on the second law thermodynamics is broken into three parts:

I. *Examine the types of energy changes that make some processes irreversible*
II. *Develop a statistical reason for irreversibility and connect this statistical approach to a thermodynamic approach*
III. *Apply the second law of thermodynamics and efficiency of processes to the analysis of thermodynamics engines and thermodynamic pumps*

For each part, we provide examples of activities that can be used in the classroom and brief discussions of anticipated student difficulties with the subject matter.

Chapter subject matter	**Related textbook section**	**ALG activities**	**End-of-chapter questions and problems**	**Videos**
Examine the types of energy changes that make some processes irreversible	13.1	13.1.1, 13.1.2, 13.2.1, 13.2.2	Questions 1, 2, 4, 6 Problems 3, 4	13.1, 13.2

Develop a statistical reason for irreversibility and connect this statistical approach to a thermodynamic approach	13.2, 13.3		Question 11 Problems 6, 7, 8, 14, 16–20	
Apply the second law of thermodynamics and efficiency of processes to the analysis of thermodynamics engines and thermodynamic pumps	13.4, 13.5	13.3.4–13.3.7, 13.4.1–13.4.5, 13.4.8	Question 9 Problems 23, 25, 28, 29, 30, 32, 34	

I. Examine the Types of Energy Changes That Make Some Processes Irreversible

In Testing Experiment Table 13.1 and Active Learning Guide (ALG) activity 13.1.1, students analyze processes that are never observed to move in the reverse direction, although those reversed processes are consistent with the first law of thermodynamics (this can be done in class with students working in groups and sharing their ideas). They find that when the processes progress in the direction that is "observed" in nature, organized energy is converted to disorganized energy. In the reverse direction, disorganized energy should be converted to more organized energy, but those processes are not observed in nature. Students encounter three more examples when they work through Conceptual Exercise 13.1. ALG activity 13.1.2 and Conceptual Exercise 13.2 engage students in very similar reasoning: which types of energy in a system are more useful? Finally, Observational Experiment Table 13.2 introduces a new variable into the discussion of the direction in which processes occur in an isolated system—energy is transferred by heating from hotter to cooler objects. Corresponding ALG activities are 13.2.1 and 13.2.2. To summarize, ALG sections 13.1 and 13.2 and the Section 13.1 help students construct three rules: (1) We do not observe conversions of the internal thermal energy of a system (kinetic energy of random motion of particles) to organized macroscopic kinetic energy or to gravitational potential energy in isolated systems; (2) We rate the usefulness of different types of system's energy in doing work on the environment; gravitational and kinetic energy are rated more useful than chemical energy of gasoline, which is more useful than random kinetic energy (thermal energy); (3) Observations show that in isolated systems, thermal energy is always transferred from hot to cool substances. These are all qualitative statements of the second law of thermodynamics. You can use end-of-chapter questions 1, 2, 4, and 6 and problems 3 and 4 in recitations and lectures in addition to the ALG activities.

II. Develop a Statistical Reason for Irreversibility and Connect This Statistical Approach to a Thermodynamic Approach

Section 13.2 and ALG activities 13.3.1 and 13.3.2 provide students with questions and exercises to learn a statistical method to count the ways in which the atoms in a gas can be divided between two halves of a box. For small numbers of atoms, the least probable distribution is with all atoms bunched together on the same half, and the most probable distribution is with equal numbers of atoms on each half. The latter is a less-organized distribution. For small numbers of particles, there is a reasonable chance for them to all be in the same half. But as the number of atoms in the box increases, it is overwhelmingly more probable for the atoms to be equally distributed between the two halves of the box. We introduce the "count" of microstates as the number of ways to have a certain number of atoms on one half and the rest on the other half (a particular macrostate). The textbook then defines the entropy of a particular macrostate as a physical quantity that is proportional to the natural logarithm (ln) of the count. Example 13.4 helps students find that the entropy increases as a fixed amount of gas expands. A more concentrated gas has more potential to do work on some other system and is more "useful." The expanded gas has less potential to do work. Thus, this increasing entropy of an expanding gas is consistent with the idea that entropy increases as a system loses its potential to do useful work on some other system. The statistical version of the second law of thermodynamics is that isolated systems tend to proceed in the direction of increasing entropy. Problems 6–8 and 14 can be used with lectures and recitations to help students understand this statistical approach.

This statistical approach becomes cumbersome if applied to large numbers of particles. In Section 13.3, we use this approach to help create a thermodynamic expression for entropy change, which involves the physical quantity of the energy transferred through heating from environment to a system and the average value of the absolute temperature of the system. This allows us to formulate the second law, which is that the sum of the entropy changes of a system and its environment must always increase during any allowed process. At the end of Section 13.3, there is a short discussion about how humans manage to grow and increase in complexity, what seems like a contradiction to the second law. You can decide if this is a brief discussion that you want to hold with your own class. Students can use the thermodynamic approach to entropy change by working on end-of-chapter question 11 and problems 16, 17, 18, 19, and 20.

III. Apply the Second Law of Thermodynamics and Efficiency of Processes to the Analysis of Motors, Refrigerators, and Heat Pumps

In Section 13.4, the first and second laws of thermodynamics along with the definitions of efficiency (and Carnot's maximum efficiency) are used to analyze thermodynamic engines, refrigerators, and thermodynamic pumps. Notice that we do not use the terms heat engines and heat pumps in order to prevent students from thinking that heat is a fluid that can be transferred from one system to another. When discussing thermodynamic pumps, it is helpful to mention that the pumps gather energy from Earth and its atmosphere. These types of renewable energy concepts are very important these days, and students have a genuine interest in them.

The second law of thermodynamics is moderately difficult material. It is important here to be careful about work. In previous chapters we agreed that the system did not do work; only the environment did work on the system—positive or negative. Here the processes are more complicated and the system and the environment interchange. When students use bar charts to analyze processes, the work represented on the bar chart is always the work done on a chosen system, but in other instances one system can work on another system. Caution students to be very careful when they talk about work. It needs to be clear what does work on what and what system is used for the analysis of energy conservation. ALG activities 13.3.4–13.3.7 and 13.4.1–13.4.4 help students master these issues.

Section 13.5 and ALG activity 13.4.5 are dedicated to the lack of efficiency of automobiles and power plants. Students can get more practice with the concepts in Sections 13.4 and 13.5 by working end-of-chapter question 9 and problems 23, 25, 28, 29, 30, 32, and 34. ALG activity 13.4.8 provides an example of a hypothetical experiment that students can design to determine the average efficiency of a human body.

14

Electric Charge, Force, and Energy

We have completed our investigations of mechanics, gases and liquids, and thermodynamics. We now start five chapters concerning electricity and magnetism. The conceptual arrangement of Chapters 14 and 15 is slightly different than most other textbooks. Chapter 14 combines the concepts of electric force and electrical potential energy, whereas Chapter 15 is dedicated to the analysis of electric field as the medium of interaction, using the quantities of $\vec{E}$ field and V field (electric potential). Both force and potential energy involve an interaction between two or more objects. How these objects interact is the action-at-a-distance problem. Chapter 15 serves as the counterpoint to this, introducing a vector field (the $\vec{E}$ field) and a scalar field (the V field) to solve the action-at-a-distance problem. We feel that students need to understand the context in which the field representation exists. Chapter 14 is broken into three parts:

I. *Qualitative analysis of electrostatic interactions of charged objects and of charged and uncharged objects, including interactions of charged particles with conductors and nonconductors (dielectrics)*
II. *Quantitative analysis of electrostatic interactions: Coulomb's force law and the electrical potential energy of systems of charged point particles*
III. *Applications of electrostatics knowledge to problems and real-life situations*

For each part, we provide examples of activities that can be used in the classroom and brief discussions of anticipated student difficulties with the subject matter.

Chapter subject matter	Related textbook section	ALG activities	End-of-chapter questions and problems	Videos
Qualitative electrostatic interactions, including interactions of charged particles with conductors and nonconductors (dielectrics)	14.1–14.3	14.1.1, 14.1.2, 14.1.4, 14.1.6–14.1.9, 14.2.1	Questions 2, 3 Problems 3, 4	14.1–14.4
Quantitative analysis of electrostatic interactions: Coulomb's force law and the electrical potential energy of systems of charged point particles	14.4, 14.5	14.2.3, 14.3.1, 14.4.1–14.4.4, 14.4.7–14.4.11	Questions 6–10 Problems 6–10, 13, 15, 16, 18, 19, 25, 29, 32, 34	
Applications of electrostatics knowledge to problems and real-life situations	14.6, 14.7	14.4.12	Problems 35, 36–41, 44–46, 49, 52, 54, 59, 62	

I. Qualitative Electrostatic Interactions, Including Interactions of Charged Particles with Conductors and Nonconductors (Dielectrics)

Electric charge exploration starts with students learning the new types of interaction. Physics instructors commonly start this chapter by letting students observe the interaction of charged objects with uncharged objects: comb and hair, a balloon rubbed with wool and a wall. Notice that in both the textbook and the Active Learning Guide (ALG), the exploration starts with objects rubbed with some other object, and only after students come up with the concept of two different types of electric charges do they proceed to the investigations of charged and uncharged objects.

To begin, students can observe and debate the patterns in the experiments described in Table 14.1 or perform ALG Experiments 14.1.1 and 14.1.2 in a lab. In both cases, students observe repulsion of the same objects rubbed with the same material as well as the attraction of objects rubbed with different materials and the object and the material with which it is rubbed. Thus, rubbing makes objects acquire a new property—to be able to attract or repel other objects after rubbing. The textbook provides a brief history of the exploration of this phenomenon and shows the term that physicists invented for this new property, electric charge. It is important that the term electric charge comes after students have had experience with the phenomenon. Students should realize that we never see electric charge—it is an invented concept to help explain the observed attractive and repulsive forces.

A summary of six observations and patterns explained by the introduction of electric charge and the electrostatic force between charged objects appears in the middle of Section 14.1. The experiments in Observational Experiment Table 14.2 help students expand their knowledge of charged objects as they observe that both positively and negatively charged objects attract uncharged objects (you can use end-of-chapter question 2 here).

The next step is for the students to come up with a mechanism explaining the interaction of charged objects. So far, students are familiar with the attraction of objects due to the gravitational force. However, many have experienced the attraction and repulsion of magnets prior to taking the physics class. If you ask students to explain why rubbed objects repel and attract each other, the most common answer will be "they are magnets." This is a very testable hypothesis. ALG activity 14.1.4 guides students through the reasoning process necessary to design an experiment to test this hypothesis. Table 14.3 in Section 14.2 summarizes the reasoning process and outcomes of a possible testing experiment. ALG activity 14.1.4 is an excellent component of a lab if you decide you want students to design their own testing experiments. Alternately, you could have students discuss and propose experiments during the lecture. You can take on the role of explaining what would actually happen if the students did the experiment they described. Note that in doing the experiments, students should find out that both poles of the magnet attract the objects rubbed with different materials. Later in the chapter, students need to return to this observation and realize that the reason for such attraction is the metal nature of the magnet; it behaves as any conductor in the presence of an electrically charged object.

Another model that students often come up with to explain the interaction is the particle model—when two objects are rubbed, one loses some particles and the other gains them, so the one that has lost "wants" them back. Although it is not a very scientific mechanism, it is basically similar to the one physicists have (except the "wanting" part), so this is a productive aspect of student reasoning on which you can build. The textbook exposes students to the fluid model of electric charge and the oil drop experiment, which indicated that electric charge came in tiny quantized units. The textbook then uses a contemporary model to explain experiments discussed in the first two sections. Students can practice these ideas by answering question 3 and doing problems 3 and 4.

Often, it is difficult for students to understand how one can charge an object positively if positively charged particles cannot be added to the object. You can help here by using a number example. A neutral object has a total zero electric charge. When one takes away a few negatively charged particles, the procedure is similar to subtracting a negative number from zero; for example, $0-(-5)$; the result is a positive number : $0-(-5)=0+5=+5$.

Students can now perform ALG activities 14.1.6–14.1.9 to develop an understanding of the internal structure of conductors and dielectrics and get familiar with how electroscopes work. ALG activity 14.1.6 starts with observational experiments similar to Observational Experiment Table 14.2. Students are asked to come up with models of the internal structure of the material that would explain why neutral objects are attracted to charged objects. This is a great activity to run in class or in lab. In class, you can ask students to propose models and discuss them with each other. The main idea here is that both conductors and dielectrics have positively and negatively charged particles inside them before they come in contact with other objects. In the presence of external charged objects, negatively charged particles in the metals move to a different location, and in dielectrics they just shift within a molecule, creating polarized molecules, or reorient if the molecule was already polarized. In both cases, a surface charge is created, but in one case it is free (conductors) and in the other case it is bound (dielectrics).

Students already have some ideas about the internal structure of materials, and in our experience they often propose the free electron model (conductors) and the polarization model (dielectrics), although they will not know which model should be associated with metals and which should be associated with insulators. Students can then use each of the two models to make predictions about the possible outcomes of testing the experiment in ALG activity 14.1.7.

Another good testing experiment involves charging one side of two touching metal soda cans and then separating them. (The experiment must be done very carefully so the cans do not get discharged during the separation.) Students need to predict what happens to the charges of the cans. Because of the movement of negative charge from one can to the other, the cans are charged oppositely. However, when the experiment is repeated with two touching plastic bottles, they do not become charged. After students have established that the free electron model applies to metals and the polarization model applies to Styrofoam and plastics, students can read Section 14.3 and apply their understanding of conductors to the behavior of electroscopes (ALG activities 14.1.8, 14.1.9, and 14.2.1).

In general, when students make predictions or reason about electrostatics phenomena, make sure they draw the distribution of charged particles inside the objects, charge diagrams, and reason qualitatively with those. The section ends with several applications: determination that the human body is a conductor, the idea of grounding, the discharge of an electroscope by polar water molecules in the air, and a review of the properties of electric charge.

II. Coulomb's Force Law and the Electrical Potential Energy of Systems of Charged Point Particles

So far, students have observed that electric forces that charged objects exert on other charged objects decrease with the increase of the distance between them. ALG activity 14.3.1 presents students with fabricated data to use in constructing Coulomb's law. The results of the analysis are given in Table 14.5 in Section 14.4, If you want students to first attempt the task on their own, it is better to start with the ALG here. Students analyze pretend data to develop an expression for the magnitude of the force that electric charge 1 exerts on electric charge 2—Coulomb's law. It is important that students realize that the law (as we have formulated it) is used only to find the magnitude of the force. The direction of the forces exerted on a particular charged object by other charged objects can be determined from a force diagram for the object of interest and by whether the forces exerted on the system object are attractive or repulsive. The signs of the charges in Coulomb's law correctly determine the direction of the force *only* in a properly defined radial coordinate system. We feel that this is too much unnecessary mathematical overhead for students. We have found that students are more comfortable with the previously described approach. Asking students to construct force diagrams for each of multiple charges is a very useful exercise (see ALG activity 14.4.1 and 14.4.2 and end-of-chapter problem 15).

Students should also understand that two charged objects exert equal magnitude and opposite direction forces on each other, even if one object has a much greater charge (see ALG activity 14.4.3 and textbook Conceptual Exercise 14.3). Finally, for problems involving charges in a plane and two-dimensional forces, it is important to use a complete problem-solving approach, which includes a sketch, force diagram, and Newton's second law in component form. Students could have forgotten this process from the first semester, and if you do such problems for electrostatics, the process needs careful review. You can use the following activities here in lectures or recitations: ALG activity 14.4.4; questions 6, 7, and 8; and problems 6, 8, 9, 10,13, 15, 16, 18, and 19.

The electrical potential energy of a system of two or more point charged objects is the subject of Section 14.5. Electrical potential energy is glossed over in many textbooks, and yet it forms the fundamental grounding and understanding for the more abstract quantity of electrical potential. In our experience, the time devoted to understanding electrical potential energy pays off later when students have to wrestle with electrical potential. Both the ALG and the textbook follow the same approach.

Student learning of electric potential energy is based on the system approach, which initially involves using bar charts to analyze situations involving electrically charged objects qualitatively. From this analysis, students invent a new type of energy—electric potential energy. Only then do they proceed to the construction of the mathematical description of this energy of two like and two unlike charged objects. We recommend starting off the section on electrical potential energy with an in-class clicker question, in which you present students with pairs of configurations of two charged objects and ask them which configuration has more electrical potential energy. For example, you could ask students to compare the electrical potential energy of a system consisting of a positively charged object and a negatively charged object when they are two different distances apart. Then you could ask students to compare the electrical potential energy of a system of two negatively charged objects (or two positively charged objects) when they are placed different distances apart. In our experience, this is a challenging activity for students because there is more than one variable involved (charge and distance), but it helps them to keep track of how electrical potential energy should increase or decrease based on the signs of the charged objects and the distance apart.

It is very important to establish the zero level of electric potential energy. For simplicity, we always assume that the electric potential energy of a system of electrically charged objects is zero when the distance between the objects is infinite. The signs of the potential energies can cause difficulties. To help students with the signs, use ALG activity 14.4.6 and textbook Example 14.6, in which students graph the potential energy versus separation distance.

At the end of the section, students meet the concept of the electrical potential energy of a system of multiple charged objects. In problem-solving sessions, students can work on ALG activities 14.4.7–14.4.11, and in lecture classes they can try end-of-chapter questions 9 and 10. These can be followed up with problems 25, 29, 32, and 34. Other end-of-chapter problems for Sections 14.6 and 14.7 can also be integrated into the instruction with Sections 14.4 and 14.5 (see the problem list at the end of Part III).

III. Skills and Applications when Applying This Knowledge in Problem Solving

Example 14.7 in Section 14.6 provides a problem-solving skill box that describes the strategies used to solve electrostatics problems and illustrates the use of the strategies for the example problem. The example involves electrostatic force. Example 14.8 uses the same strategies for an energy problem—radon decay in the lungs.

Section 14.7 has more examples: the operation of a Van de Graaff generator, a free electron acceleration near a Van de Graaff that causes atom ionization and a 10-cm long spark, the operation of a Wimshurst generator, and a photocopy machine. Many of the end-of-chapter problems in these two sections are actually appropriate for use in Sections 14.4 and 14.5 and can be applied with students in lectures or in recitations, including problems 35, 36–41, 44, 45, 46, 49, 52, 54, 59, and 62. You can end the chapter with a short lab described in ALG activity 14.4.12.

15

The Electric Field

In Chapter 14, students developed ideas concerning electric charge, force, and energy using a point charge action-at-a-distance interaction model. In this chapter, they learn a field approach for these same interactions—especially important for the electric circuit analysis in Chapter 16. This chapter is broken into five parts:

I. *Qualitative and quantitative development of the electric field concept and the quantity of the $\vec{E}$ field*
II. *Development of the physical quantity of electric potential V (V field), using it to analyze processes, and relating the electric field and the V field*
III. *Conductors and dielectrics in electric fields*
IV. *Capacitors*
V. *Applying these ideas to understand electrocardiography and lightning*

For each part, we provide examples of activities that can be used in the classroom and brief discussions of anticipated student difficulties with the subject matter.

Chapter subject matter	**Related textbook section**	**ALG activities**	**End-of-chapter questions and problems**	**Videos**
Qualitative and quantitative development of the electric field concept and the quantity of the $\vec{E}$ field	15.1, 15.2	15.1.1–15.1.4, 15.2.1, 15.2.3, 15.2.6, 15.2.7, 15.4.1–15.4.4	Question 1 Problems 3, 4, 6–8, 12, 14, 16, 19, 20, 60	15.1

Development of the electric potential V (V field), using it to analyze processes, and relating the $\vec{E}$ field and the V field	15.3, 15.4	15.4.7, 15.2.10–15.2.13, 15.3.1, 15.3.2	Problems 24, 26, 28, 31, 32, 33, 62	15.2
Conductors and dielectrics in electric fields	15.5, 15.6	15.3.2, 15.3.3, 15.2.9	Question 3 Problems 34, 36, 37, 44, 48	
Capacitors	15.7		Problems 47–50, 54	
Applying these ideas to understand electrocardiography and lightning	15.8	15.4	Problems 56, 58	

Before we proceed to the analysis of individual sections and activities, we should discuss the language used in this chapter. Because students have tremendous difficulties with the concept of field as "altered space" and the concept of electric potential, we have moved away from the traditional terminology. We wish to help students conceptually distinguish between the ideas that (1) there is an altered region of space (altered by the presence of one or more electrically charged objects) with specific properties and (2) each point in this region of space can be described by several physical quantities. We will use the term *field* (electric or some other field) to describe an altered region of space. We call the physical quantity, which is traditionally called electric field, $\vec{E}$ field, and we call the quantity traditionally called electric potential V field (and electric potential). The former is the force-like vector quantity, and the latter is the energy-like scalar quantity. We represent $\vec{E}$ field with $\vec{E}$ field vectors and E field lines and V field with equipotential surfaces. In summary, when charged objects are present, each point in space can be described by a vector field($\vec{E}$ field) and a scalar field (V field).

I. Qualitative Development of the Concept of Electric Field and Quantitative Development of the Physical Quantity of $\vec{E}$ Field

To help students create the concept of the field as the medium for interactions, both the textbook and the Active Learning Guide (ALG) start by establishing the analogy between gravitational and electrostatic interactions (Section 15.1 and ALG activities 15.1.1–15.1.2) and the activities that help students devise a field-based model for both. In this model, an electrically charged object creates a disturbance in space. When another object is placed in this disturbance, its motion is affected. Thus, two charged objects can interact with each other without direct contact (the same logic applies to the objects with mass, although we do not distinguish between gravitational and inertial mass). ALG activities 15.1.3 and 15.1.4 ask the students to use the field model of electrostatic interaction to explain the described experiments and to design new experiments in which metal objects act as shields. After students have constructed the concept of the field as the medium for interactions, they learn two physical quantities that characterize the field—the force-type quantity of $\vec{E}$ field and energy-type quantity of V field. Here again we rely on the analogy between the electric and gravitational fields (ALG activity 15.2.1). To help students develop the physical quantity of $\vec{E}$ field at a particular location that students should conceptualize as the force that would be exerted on a unit charge placed at that location, we first use the case of the field created by one electrically charged object (called the source) and analyze the forces exerted on another object (the test object) that is placed in the field. We rely on the analogy with the idea of a gravitational field:

$$\vec{g} = \frac{\vec{F}_{\text{Field on Object}}}{m_{\text{Object}}} \text{ and } \vec{E}_{\text{due to } Q} = \frac{\vec{F}_{Q\text{field on } q_{\text{test}}}}{q_{\text{test}}}$$

Notice that both equations represent operational definitions for the $\vec{g}$ field and $\vec{E}$ field at a particular location. It is important to label the test object with a special subscript to avoid confusion (we continue to stress the difference between the source and test objects throughout the chapter). To devise the cause-effect relationships that explain the value of the $\vec{g}$ field and $\vec{E}$ fields and show that those values do not depend on the test objects, students use the law of universal gravitation and Coulomb's law.

Observational Experiment Table 15.1 helps students devise the superposition principle for $\vec{E}$ fields. Following it, Reasoning Skill 1 indicates how to estimate graphically the net $\vec{E}$ field due to multiple charges, including an example of the field due to an electric dipole on the heart at one instant during the heartbeat cycle (students can do ALG activities 15.1.2 and 15.2.3 here; textbook Conceptual Exercise 15.1 is a worked example for ALG activity 15.2.3).

So far, students represent electric field quantitatively and graphically with $\vec{E}$ field vectors. The next step is to learn to represent it with $\vec{E}$ field lines (the introduction is in the textbook subsection; students can then do ALG activities 15.2.6 and 15.2.7). We use this representation because it allows students to form concrete images of the abstract concept. To draw a line, students need to first draw $\vec{E}$ field vectors at several locations and then draw the line to which those vectors are tangent. Conceptual Exercise 15.2 helps students draw the $\vec{E}$ field lines for a large, uniformly charged glass plate.

Section 15.2 illustrates methods for solving two common types of problems involving $\vec{E}$ fields:

(1) In some problems a source charge distribution is given, and students are asked to determine the $\vec{E}$ field at a particular location. Students could have forgotten how to add vector components; thus, it is important to go slowly through such a problem-solving process. The process is summarized in Reasoning Skill 2 and is illustrated in the text in Example 15.3. You can start with ALG activities 15.4.1–15.4.2 and then have students review at home the worked example and follow up with the *Try It Yourself* activity for that example, which is also done in steps, with answers for each step.

(2) The second type of problem involves analyzing a process involving various forces, including forces caused by a given $\vec{E}$ field. A problem-solving strategy is outlined on the left side of the table in Example 15.4 and illustrated for a problem on the right side of the table. The strategy is used again in Example 15.5 to determine the deflection of a tiny charged ink ball in an ink-jet printer. Students in a lecture can try end-of-chapter question 1and work on ALG activities 15.4.3–15.4.4. Homework can be problems 3, 4, 6, 7, 8, 12, 14, 16, 19, 20, and 60.

II. Developing the Physical Quantity of V Field (Electric Potential), Using It to Analyze Processes, and Relating the $\vec{E}$ Field and the V Field

We follow the same logic when helping students develop the concept of another quantity characterizing electric field at each location. The $\vec{E}$ field at a particular location describes a force that the field would exert on a unit charge (or force divided by the test charge, assuming that the test charge is positive) placed at that location, and the quantity of V field at a particular location describes the energy that the field-unit charge system would have if a unit test charge were placed at that location. In Section 15.3, students find that the ratio of the electric potential energy of the system of a source charge Q and a test charge q separated by distance r and the test charge ($(kQq/r)/q = kQ/r$) is independent of the test charge. Thus, it can represent an energy field (we call it V field) at a distance r from the source charge. ALG activity 15.4.7 and textbook Quantitative Exercise 15.6 help students develop the concept of superposition of the V field due to multiple charges by determining the V field (electric potential) in body tissue caused by the dipole charge on the heart. Students will be happy that the V field is a scalar quantity, and they can simply add it for multiple source charges. However, the sign of the V field at some point due to a source charge depends on the sign of the source charge.

The potential difference between two points in space is especially important in problem solving. Positively charged particles tend to move toward regions with lower potential, and negative particles tend to move toward regions with higher electric potential. This idea is used in Example 15.7 in the analysis of an X-ray machine. Section 15.3 ends with an introduction to equipotential surfaces (analogous to gravitational contour maps) and their behavior relative to electric field lines. Students need to be cautioned about this analogy: Positively charged objects travel "downhill," but negatively charged objects travel "uphill." Students can come to grips with this rather strange idea, but it does require some attention from the instructor. In lecture classes, you can try end-of-chapter question 4 and in recitations or lectures students can work on ALG activities 15.2.10–15.2.13 and textbook problems 24, 26, 28, 31, 32, 33, and 62.

In Section 15.4, students derive a quantitative relation $\vec{E}$ field and V field ($E_x = -\Delta V / \Delta x$). Testing Experiment Table 15.2 uses the spark distance for a Van de Graaff generator to test the relation. Related ALG activities are 15.3.1 and 15.3.2.

III. Conductors and Dielectrics in Electric Field

The logical progression of Section 15.5 and matching activities in the ALG is electric field of a charged conductor (ALG activity 15.3.2), grounding (ALG activity 15.3.3), and a conductor in an external electric field–shielding (ALG activity 15.2.9).

First students learn that charged conductors produce electric fields with $\vec{E}$ field vectors perpendicular to their surfaces. Then they reason that the $\vec{E}$ field inside a charged conductor must be zero and the V field must be constant. They then apply these ideas to explain why grounding some potentially charged electric device causes almost all of the charge to be transferred to the Earth. Students encountered the idea of grounding in Chapter 14, but that chapter did not explain it quantitatively. The concept of all points of a charged conductor having the same value of the V field helps students explain the grounding quantitatively by analyzing the redistribution of charges on the surfaces of two unequal size spherical conductors. This is a unique exercise, and we suggest that you start it with ALG activity 15.3.3 and then let students work through the textbook material in the subsection "Electric field of a charged conductor" and work on end-of-chapter problem 36. In this section, students also learn that the ratio of charge/surface area is greater on a small surface than on a larger surface to which it is connected—an idea used later to understand how lightning rods work. To develop the concept of shielding, students can start with ALG activity 15.2.9 and proceed with textbook problem 37 and then read the textbook material.

Section 15.6 is dedicated to the effect of electric fields on dielectric nonconducting materials. We discuss the polarization of the electric charge in atoms with the reorientation of permanent molecular dipoles leading to internal fields in the dielectrics with $\vec{E}$ field vectors pointing opposite the $\vec{E}$ field vectors of the external fields causing the polarization. This leads to the introduction of the dielectric constant and a reduction in the force between charged objects when in a dielectric material. This is important in biology because salts, which do not dissolve when in air, dissolve into sodium and chlorine ions when in blood. You can use end-of-chapter question 3 and Problems 34, 36, 44, and 48 to help students practice ideas from Sections 15.5 and 15.6.

IV. Capacitors

Section 15.7 is dedicated to capacitors: their general nature, the electric field between the plates separated by a distance d, the operational definition of the capacitance as $C = q/|\Delta V|$, and the cause-effect relation $C_{\text{Parallel plate capacitor}} = \frac{\kappa A}{4\pi k d}$ that explains how the capacitance depends on the physical properties of the capacitor (the area of the plates, the distance separating them, and the dielectric constant of the material separating them). We make a connection to biology in Example 15.10 that explores the capacitance of body cells estimated along with the total electric charge separated from the inside to the outside of the cell walls. Toward the end of Section 15.7, we derive an expression for the energy stored by charge separation of capacitor plates and then apply it to estimate the energy stored by the charge separation across body cells. Finally, an expression for the energy density stored in an electric field is developed. Problems 47, 48, 49, 50, and 54 can be used with students in lectures and recitations.

V. Applying These Ideas to Understand Electrocardiography and Lightning

Section 15.8 applies the chapter ideas to two interesting phenomena: how electrocardiographs, with pads placed on the skin, are able to monitor the operation of the heart deep inside the body; and how lightning rods work (also recommendations for what to do outside when lightning is occurring). You can ask students to address end-of-chapter problems 56 and 58 at the end of this chapter and to practice the remaining activities in Section 15.4 of the ALG.

16

DC Circuits

In Chapter 15, students learned two physical quantities that describe the electric field quantitatively—$\vec{E}$ field and V field–electric potential. They also learned that an electrically charged particle will accelerate if placed in the region with an electric field. In this chapter, students extend this idea to the motion of electric charge in electric circuits. We have broken the chapter into four parts, with the early focus on qualitative reasoning and the latter on quantitative problem solving:

I. *Electric current, batteries, simple circuits, Ohm's law, and qualitative analysis of circuits*
II. *Joule's law, Kirchhoff's rules, series and parallel circuits, and skills for quantitatively solving circuit problems*
III. *Properties of resistors, superconductivity, and semiconductors*
IV. *Modeling the human circulatory system as an electric circuit, and circuit breakers*

For each part, we provide examples of activities that can be used in the classroom and brief discussions of the motivations for using these activities.

Chapter subject matter	**Related textbook section**	**ALG activities**	**End-of-chapter questions and problems**	**Videos**
Electric current, batteries, simple circuits, Ohm's law, and qualitative analysis of circuits	16.1–16.5	16.1.1–16.1.7, 16.2.1–16.2.7, 16.3.1, 16.3.2	Questions 1–10	16.1, 16.2, 16.3, 16.4, 16.5, 16.6

Joule's law, Kirchhoff's rules, series and parallel circuits, and skills for quantitatively solving circuit problems	16.6–16.9	16.3.6, 16.3.8, 16.3.9, 16.4.1–16.4.3, 16.3.14, 16.4.11–16.4.13	Problems 11–13, 15–18, 21–36, 38–39, 41–44, 72	16.7
Properties of resistors, superconductivity, and semiconductors	16.10		Problems 47–49, 51, 53, 56	
Modeling the human circulatory system as an electric circuit, and circuit breakers	16.11		Problems 57–60	

I. Electric Current, Batteries, Simple Circuits, Ohm's Law, and Qualitative Analysis of Circuits

It is important to start the development of concepts related to electric circuits by building qualitative understanding. Research shows that students who can solve complex problems involving multiple current loops often do not understand circuits conceptually. Thus textbook Sections 16.1–16.5 and Active Learning Guide (ALG) Sections 16.1 and 16.2 focus on this qualitative understanding.

The first step is to understand that while potential difference between two locations is necessary for electrically charged particles to relocate, the motion of charges due to an electric field leads to the equalizing of potentials, which stops this movement. ALG activities 16.1.1–16.1.4 and textbook Observational Experiment Table 16.1 in Section 16.1 help to provide students with this understanding. These experiments can be done in labs or in lectures and serve as a bridge between electrostatics and DC circuits. By analyzing the patterns in the experiments, students infer the charge transfer by analyzing the position of the electroscope leaves, the motion of a light metal-coated ball, or the light from a neon bulb.

Students' analysis of the experiments should lead them to the conclusion that if there is potential difference between two points in some region and charged particles that can move in this region, this motion leads to a spark, a glow of a neon bulb, or some mechanical motion of a conducting object. However, all of these effects are short-lived as the motion of the charged particles in the electric field leads to the equalizing of potentials.

To help students visualize this process, the textbook makes an analogy of the water flow between two containers, in which water is at different heights, emphasizing that it is not the difference in the amount of liquid in the containers but the pressure difference (the height of the water in the containers) that makes the water flow, due to the gravitational pull of Earth. After the levels of the water in the containers equalize, no more water will flow, because of the pull of Earth. The water must be manually lifted up to continue the process. This analogy helps students understand the role of a battery in a circuit (ALG activity 16.1.5). Note that this analogy works best if students have thoroughly learned and understood the chapters on fluid statics and dynamics. Testing experiments for the role of the battery concepts are in ALG activities 16.1.6 and 16.1.7 and can be done in a lab.

Textbook Section 16.2 continues the analysis of the role of a battery in a simple circuit and introduces the idea of emf as the work per unit charge that a battery does to maintain potential difference in a circuit. Note Conceptual Exercise 16.2 in this section—it introduces the students to graphing of potential along the circuit. End-of-chapter problems 2, 3, and 8 can be used with students in lectures or recitations.

In Section 16.3, students look for a pattern in the way a wire and battery can be connected to get a flashlight bulb to light (there is a similar activity in ALG activity 16.1.5). This leads to the idea of a complete circuit. It is best if every student actually goes through the exercise described in Observational Experiment Table 16.2 before reading the textbook. After those exercises, students can work on ALG activities 16.2.1–16.2.3 to develop a better understanding of the role of different elements in a circuit through analogical reasoning. Following this step, students learn the symbols for various circuit elements and learn how the devices work that measure current and potential difference.

So far, students have learned a lot about circuits, but all of the explorations and reasoning were qualitative. Observational Experiment Table 16.3 and ALG activity 16.3.1 show students pretend data for the electric current through a commercial resistor and the potential difference across the same resistor. These activities are best done in a lab when students can actually collect the data and look for patterns in the data (make sure you use commercial resistors in the lab). Analysis of the patterns leads them to the idea that current through the resistor is proportional to the potential difference across it, and the inverse of the proportionality coefficient is the new physical quantity of resistance ($R = (\Delta V)/I$ is an operational definition of resistance). Note that later we will write Ohm's law as $I = 1/R(\Delta V) = (\Delta V)/R$ to underscore the cause-effect relationship: A current I is the result of a potential difference ΔV.

In ALG activity 16.3.2, students can test whether the behavior of a light bulb filament is correctly predicted by Ohm's law. Although students only start building microscopic models of resistance in Section 16.10, the variable resistance of the light bulb is a great opportunity to get students thinking about building those microscopic models. Note that students most likely will not make a connection between the brightness of the light bulb and the temperature of the filament. They need some explicit prompting to think about it while they are trying to explain why the resistance increases as the bulb gets brighter. The textbook adds to testing Ohm's law for other circuit elements, such as diodes and, most importantly, for an open circuit. Students often think that if there is no current in a circuit, the potential difference across any element is zero. ALG activities 16.4.10 and 16.4.11 address the same goal. You can use end-of-chapter problems 9, 10, 11, and 13 in lectures and recitations.

ALG activities 16.2.4–16.2.7 and textbook Section 16.5 introduce students to simple circuits in which flashlight bulbs are wired in series and in parallel. Here the brightness of bulbs is used as an indicator of the relative electric current through the bulbs. There are a few important ideas that students need to understand here: specifically, that the battery is not a source of constant current but is a source of almost constant potential difference, and that current is not used up in series circuits but is the same through each element. Note that students tend to reason about electric circuits using current as the fundamental concept, although it is more productive to base the analysis on potential difference. Analysis of the circuits leads to a list of qualitative rules based on the experiments (see the list after Table 16.6). In Conceptual Exercise 16.5, students use the rules to reason qualitatively to predict the relative brightness of bulbs in a more complex circuit. You can use textbook end-of-chapter questions 1–10 and ALG activities 16.1.8 and 16.2.4–16.2.7 in lectures or recitations to help develop students' qualitative understanding of electric circuits. Alternatively, students can conduct lab experiments similar to the ALG activities. The section ends by considering the wiring in a home.

II. Joule's Law, Kirchhoff's Rules, Series and Parallel Circuits, and Skills for Quantitatively Solving Circuit Problems

Sections 16.6–16.6.9 help students construct a quantitative understanding of electric circuits. In Section 16.6, they learn how to derive an expression for the rate of electric energy conversion (the electric power) of a circuit element. To start thinking about power, we suggest that the students observe or perform the experiment described at the beginning of textbook Section 16.6, in which two *different* light bulbs are connected in series. As so far students have only had identical light bulbs in all experiments, they know that identical bulbs in series have the same brightness, which they explained as being the result of the same current through the bulbs. Now students observe that the bulbs in series have different brightness despite the fact that the current through them is the same. This finding suggests the question of what affects the brightness of the bulb. ALG activity 16.3.8 helps students derive the expression for power, and ALG activity 16.3.9 is the testing experiment. End-of-chapter problems 18, 21, 22, and 72 can be used with students in lectures or recitations.

Section 16.7 is dedicated to Kirchhoff's loop and junction rules. This is also the section where students first encounter the concept of the internal resistance of the battery (Example 16.7). Students devise the rules by analyzing simple circuits (ALG activities 16.3.6, 16.4.1, and 16.4.2). Some textbooks introduce Kirchhoff's rules *after* students learn how to add resistors in series and parallel. We feel that it makes more sense for students to explore Kirchhoff's rules *before* adding resistors in series and parallel because deriving the mathematical expressions requires Kirchhoff's rules. Note the summary of the sign conventions for using Kirchhoff's rules in a margin note before the introduction of the loop rule.

It is important when using Kirchhoff's rules to indicate with arrows the anticipated directions of the current in each branch of a circuit. The signs of potential changes across resistive elements when using the loop rule depend on the way the loop is being traversed relative to the anticipated direction of the current. If the current direction is chosen incorrectly but the potential changes across resistive elements is included correctly in the loop rule, an error in current direction choice will just yield a negative sign when Kirchhoff's rules are solved for the current. Note ALG activities 16.4.3 and 16.4.14 and end-of-chapter problems 15–17, 23–29, 30, and 31 that can be used with students in recitations and lectures. Be sure that students add current direction arrows to their circuit diagrams and use the sign conventions correctly.

The textbook uses Kirchhoff's rules to derive the equivalent resistance of series and parallel resistive parts of circuits (Section 16.8). Note that Example 16.8 returns to the brightness of series and parallel circuits of bulbs but is done quantitatively. Example 16.10 helps develop the ability to break a complex group of resistive elements into equivalent series and parallel resistances. End-of-chapter problems 32–36 can be used with students in lectures and recitations.

Example 16.9 in Section 16.9 shows how to adapt the general multiple problem-solving strategy to electric circuit problems. It is applied again for a circuit, which involves series and parallel resistive elements in Example 16.10. You can use end-of-chapter questions 11–13 and problems 38, 39, and 41–44 in lectures and recitations. ALG activities 16.4.11–16.4.12 and the lab described in activity 16.4.13 are excellent in helping students to put the ideas together. Note that one of most common difficulties that students have with electric circuits is approaching the problems locally. They look only at the change that occurs when a resistor is added to the circuit at the location of that resistor. Understanding that everything in the circuit changes, including the current, is very important. Therefore, it is very useful to discuss with the students the local and global changes that occur when an element is added or removed from the circuit. This discussion can occur when students work on any problem involving a complex circuit.

III. Properties of Resistors, Superconductivity, and Semiconductors

Section 16.10 concerns resistive elements, including the effect of the shape and material on the resistance of a normal resistor, the microscopic nature of resistance, the history of superconductivity, and a discussion of semiconductors. End-of-chapter problems 47–49, 51, 53, and 56 are appropriate here.

IV. Modeling the Human Circulatory System as an Electric Circuit, and Circuit Breakers

The last section in the chapter (Section 16.11) applies what was learned earlier in this chapter (and a little in former chapters) to two main problems: (1) the modeling of the human circulatory system as an electric circuit, and (2) an analysis of the role of circuit breakers in home wiring systems. End-of-chapter problems 57–60 can be used with students in lectures and recitations.

17

Magnetism

In Chapter 14, students learned about the action-at-a-distance electrostatic interaction between charged objects considered as point particles. In Chapter 15, they learned how to use a field approach to describe this interaction. In this chapter, students learn how moving charged particles produce magnetic fields and how those fields exert forces on the moving particles. Students also learn how to analyze magnetic interactions. The chapter is broken into five parts:

I. *A qualitative description of magnetic interactions and magnetic fields*
II. *The magnetic force exerted by a field on a current-carrying wire and on a moving charged object*
III. *A quantitative rule for magnetic fields created by electric currents*
IV. *Skills for analyzing magnetic processes, including important applications involving magnetic and electric fields*
V. *Properties of magnetic materials*

Chapter subject matter	**Related textbook section**	**ALG activities**	**End-of-chapter questions and problems**	**Videos**
A qualitative description of magnetic interactions and magnetic fields	17.1, 17.2	17.1.1–17.1.5, 17.2.4	Question 2	17.1, 17.2
The magnetic force exerted by a field on a current-carrying wire and on a moving charged object	17.3, 17.4	17.1.6–17.1.10, 17.2.1–17.2.3, 17.2.6, 17.2.10, 17.3.1–17.3.4, 17.3.6, 17.4.3–17.4.5, 17.4.7	Questions 3, 9, 21 Problems 3, 6–9, 11, 14, 15, 17, 19, 20, 22, 23, 25, 26	

A quantitative rule for magnetic fields created by electric currents	17.5		Problems 27, 28, 30, 31	
Skills for analyzing magnetic processes, including important applications involving magnetic and electric fields	17.6		Problems 32–39, 40–46, 48, 49	
Properties of magnetic materials	17.8			

For each part, we describe the logical sequence of the creating of new ideas and provide examples of activities that you can use in the labs, lectures, and problem-solving recitations. We also discuss student difficulties and motivation for both the Active Learning Guide (ALG) and textbook activities.

I. A Qualitative Description of Magnetic Interactions and Magnetic Fields

Textbook Section 17.1 and ALG activities 17.1.1, 17.1.2, and 17.1.4 introduce students to the phenomenon of magnetism. ALG activity 17.1.1 helps students to characterize the interaction of a compass needle with permanent magnets of different shapes. It builds the first step to the representation of a magnetic field in space with the arrow pointing from S to N inside the compass (without naming the magnetic field). ALG activities 17.1.2 and 17.1.4 focus students' attention on the differences between electrostatic and magnetic interactions. If you want to devote laboratory or recitation time to introducing magnetism, students should start with the ALG activities while using the textbook as summary reading.

Textbook Section 17.2 introduces the students to the concept of magnetic field, the physical quantity of the $\vec{B}$ field, and the compass needle as an indicator of the magnetic field in the region. Unlike an electric field, whose vector characteristic preceded the concept of electric field lines, the $\vec{B}$ field lines come up before any quantities. The textbook uses multiple compass needles to define the direction of the $\vec{B}$ field lines (the needles are tangent to the lines at every point) and gives rules for how they relate to the intensity of the $\vec{B}$ field. A fun and useful activity that can be done in recitation or a studio classroom is to have groups of students use compasses to map $\vec{B}$ field lines of different configurations of permanent magnets (such as dipole, quadrupole, and horseshoe) on portable whiteboards and present their results to the rest of the class. Make sure the magnets are very strong because students can be confused by the additional interaction of Earth's magnetic field. (Watch for conduit pipes under tables, too!). If you want to encourage students to explore magnetism, we recommend cow magnets as the most economical, safe, and student-proof magnets we have encountered.

The next step is to establish that current-carrying wires produce a magnetic effect on a compass similar to that of a permanent magnet. Students can read about the experiments in Observational Experiment Table 17.1. Activity 17.1.3 mirrors the historical experiment done by Oersted. Students observe the effect that the current-carrying wire exerts on the orientation of the compass and find patterns in that orientation. As a lecture demonstration, students can watch you perform the experiment while they look for patterns. Orient the wire without current along the natural orientation of the compass (aligned with Earth's magnetic field), so that when you turn on the current, the students can observe the biggest deflection. It is even better to arrange these conditions for individual groups. ALG activity 17.1.5 helps students visualize the "circles" for the field lines using a wire and iron filings. If you want to map the field around a wire with compasses, it is best to conduct a carefully prepared lecture demonstration. A current of at least 15A–20A is needed to swamp the effect of Earth's magnetic field. Appropriate precautions should obviously be taken. Both activities lead to a right-hand rule for determining the direction of the $\vec{B}$ field lines produced by an electric current in a wire.

Textbook Example 17.1 uses the newly established right-hand rule to determine the $\vec{B}$ field lines produced by the current in a solenoid. The $\vec{B}$ field lines produced by a bar magnet are found to be very similar to the field lines produced by the current in a coil of wire—a useful idea needed later in the chapter. ALG activity 17.2.4 and textbook question 2 provide extra practice or formative assessment.

II. The Magnetic Force Exerted by a Field on a Current-Carrying Wire and on a Moving Charged Object

After students learn that current-carrying wires create magnetic fields around them with the lines similar to permanent magnets, the next step is to investigate how magnetic fields affect the current-carrying wires and individual moving electrically charged particles. This investigation happens in two parts. Students develop a qualitative right-hand rule for the force and then develop quantitative expressions for the force exerted by the magnetic field on a current-carrying wire ($F_{\vec{B} \text{ on W}} \propto IL \sin\theta$).

The textbook's Observational Experiment Table 17.2 and ALG activities 17.1.6 and 17.1.7 provide data and observational experiments that students can use to construct a rule relating the direction of the force to the direction of the current/moving charges and the direction of the $\vec{B}$ field. Alternately, you can bring an old CRT oscilloscope to class and have students observe how the beam is deflected by the presence of a magnetic field. If you decide to have students develop a hand rule using an oscilloscope experiment like ALG activity 17.1.6 (a lengthy process), make sure that they draw the direction of the $\vec{B}$ field and the moving charges very clearly. It is at this point that you should introduce the new notation of the circle with a cross or a dot that describes a vector pointing into or out of the page, respectively.

It is important to remember that students may develop a very different hand rule than the one used in the textbook. Offer them the textbook right-hand rule for the magnetic force at the end of class discussion with the justification that communication will be easier if just one hand rule is used, and then stick to it.

The jumping wire experiment (ALG activity 17.1.8) is an excellent testing experiment in which students can immediately test the new right-hand rule and get practice in applying it at the same time. This is best done as a lecture demonstration. Give students enough time to struggle through their first attempt to apply the right-hand rule and make predictions before they actually perform the experiment. Testing Experiment Table 17.3 is very effective if you turn it into a large, spectacular lecture demonstration. Give students enough time to make their predictions before the experiment is performed.

ALG activities 17.1.9, 17.1.10, and 17.2.1–17.2.3 help students to develop and practice the right-hand rule for the force. Some of these activities can be assigned for recitations or homework. ALG activities 17.1.9 and 17.1.10 are especially important because they also serve as the starting point for later discussions about the torque exerted by a magnetic field on a loop of wire with a current flowing in it. This is the second right-hand rule that students develop in this chapter, and often they confuse the two. One way to help is that every time they use a rule, explicitly ask whether they are interested in the field created by a known source (right-hand rule for the field) or in the force that the field whose source is unknown exerts on the test object (right-hand rule for the force).

Students struggle to distinguish between the source of the field and the test object that is interacting with the field. This is likely because the distinction is a choice of perspective. Whatever the reason, some students become fixated on the idea that either one magnetic field exerts a force on another magnetic field or one wire exerts a force on the other, totally ignoring the idea that the magnetic field is the intermediary. ALG activity 17.2.6 targets all these difficulties.

Students find ALG 17.2.6 surprisingly challenging, and it is worth devoting considerable time to having them work through it. You will probably need to keep reminding them to draw the field lines produced by the source and *then* focus on the direction of the field line *at the specific point* where the (test) wire is placed.

The second part of Section 17.3 helps develop a quantitative expression for the force that a magnetic field exerts on a current-carrying wire. It is important to note here that we have not established an operational definition for the magnitude of the $\vec{B}$ field vector; yet this procedure will appear as the result of the analysis described below. Table 17.4 provides data for an imaginary experiment in which a current-carrying wire is placed in a uniform magnetic field produced by an electromagnet that does not change during the experiment. Students analyze the data to arrive at the conclusion that the magnitude of the force exerted on the current-carrying wire is directly proportional to the magnitude of the current, the length of wire, and the sine of the angle between the direction of the current and the direction of the $\vec{B}$ field vector ($F_{\vec{B}\text{ on W}} \propto IL\sin\theta$). In other words, students find that

$$\frac{F_{\vec{B}\text{ on W}}}{IL\sin\theta} = const.$$

This coefficient of proportionality that is independent of the properties of the wire but depends on the strength of the magnet is used to define the magnitude of the $\vec{B}$ field vector.

Note that the approach in the ALG is different: activity 17.3.1 provides students with the data to construct the relationship $F_{\vec{B}\text{ on W}} = ILB\sin\theta$ directly, without an intermediate step as the textbook provides. You can choose either approach here.

ALG activity 17.3.3 serves as a good lab to test the relation for the force, if you have the apparatus. If you get students to do the experiment in a lab, the best force-measuring device is a digital scale that measures to 0.01g. Using the scale to determine the force that the magnet exerts on the wire is a great opportunity for students to go back to drawing force diagrams and applying Newton's third and second laws. Students might make the wrong prediction the first time around if they have not fully realized that the right-hand rule gives the direction of the force exerted by the magnet on the wire, not the force exerted by the wire on the magnet. This is a mistake that many can figure out on their own if you give them enough time.

After establishing the expression for the force, the textbook shows how to apply the expression to solve one standard problem and then uses it to develop an expression for the torque that a magnetic field exerts on a current loop. The students can read how the torque relation explains how a DC electric motor and an ammeter work (ALG activity 17.3.4; if you have an old analogue ammeter, they can reverse-engineer it before reading the text). Students can practice the force ideas by working on ALG activity 17.4.6, and textbook end-of-chapter problems 3, 6, 7, 8, 9, 11, 14, 15, and 17. If you have time, a great application experiment lab is to give students a neodymium magnet, a kebab skewer (for the shaft), a shoe box (for mounting the motor), tape, paper clips (for brushes), and solenoid wire and have them construct a working DC motor on their own using what they've learned.

The next step is to develop the relationship for the force exerted on a moving charged particle. If you have the necessary equipment, students can start by performing ALG activity 17.1.6 to see that the right-hand rule for the magnetic force needs to be adjusted when the moving particles have a negative sign and then proceed to ALG activity 17.3.2 to deduce the quantitative relation for the force using pretend data. Section 17.4 describes experiments similar to those in ALG activity 17.1.6 and provides theoretical derivation for the magnitude of the force that the magnetic field exerts on a single moving charged particle starting with the force that the field exerts on moving charges in a wire. This leads to an expression for the magnitude and direction of the magnetic force that the field exerts on a moving charged object, considered as a point object.

The book then proceeds to study circular motion of charged particles in the magnetic field and specifically to the deflection of cosmic rays by the Earth's magnetic field (Example 17.4) and to the understanding of aurorae. Students really enjoy understanding how the aurorae work. It helps to start students off with a simpler situation of a uniform magnetic field and ask them what sort of trajectory a charged particle will take if it approaches that field in any direction other than 90 degrees to the field. Students might have difficulty putting together circular motion in the x and y directions, with uniform linear motion in the z direction to get a spiral or helix. Once they can grasp this, Example 17.4 will be much easier for them to understand. You can use ALG activities 17.2.10, 17.4.3, 17.4.4, 17.4.5, and 17.4.7 and textbook end-of-chapter questions 3, 9, and 21, and problems 19, 20, 22, 23, 25, and 26.

It is worth noting here that unlike an electric field that has only one test object (a detector), a positively charged object, the magnetic field, can have four different test objects—a compass (a qualitative detector) and a current-carrying straight wire, a current-carrying loop, and an individual moving charged particle. Unlike the single operational definition for $\vec{E}$ field as $\vec{E} = \vec{F}_{\text{source on test}} / q_{\text{test}}$, which defines both the direction and the magnitude, the direction of the $\vec{B}$ field in this book is determined through either the right-hand rule for the fields (directly) or indirectly using the right-hand rule for the force if the force is known (the book does not use vector product). The magnitude can be determined through several operational definitions: $B = \frac{F_{\vec{B}\text{ on W max}}}{IL}$, or $B = \frac{|\tau_{\vec{B}\text{ on Coil max}}|}{NAI}$, or $B = \frac{F_{\vec{B}\text{ on q max}}}{qv}$.

III. A Quantitative Rule for Magnetic Fields Created by Electric Currents

Observational Experiment Table 17.5 in Section 17.5 helps students develop an expression for the magnitude of the $\vec{B}$ field created by a long, straight wire. The proportionality constant in that equation involves the magnetic permeability of the space surrounding the location of the magnetic field. The textbook then adapts the expression for the magnitude of the $\vec{B}$ field caused by a long wire to other current situations and in particular to estimate the magnitude of the $\vec{B}$ field due to the circular electron current in a hydrogen atom (13 tesla!). Students can work on end-of-chapter problems 27, 28, 30, and 31.

IV. Skills for Analyzing Magnetic Processes Including Important Applications Involving Magnetic and Electric Fields

Example 17.6 in Section 17.6 shows how to adapt the general problem-solving strategy to problems involving magnetism. The problem involves the force that a magnetic field exerts on a clothesline. Example 17.7 is a problem that involves using the strategy to determine an unknown magnetic field. End-of-chapter problems 32, 33–38, and 49 can be used with students in lectures and recitations. Problem 39 represents a great laboratory experiment.

In Section 17.7, use the strategy to explain several important applications. Many of these involve a charged particle (ion) that moves through a perpendicular magnetic field. The field deflects positive ions to one side of the vessel through which the charged particles are moving and negative ions to the other side. These opposite charges on opposite walls cause an electric field that causes a balancing electric force—the ions now move straight ahead. This idea is used to describe magnetohydrodynamic power generation, magnetic flow meters that have no moving parts, blood flow rate meters, and a part of mass spectrometers (Quantitative Exercise 17.10), which are all discussed in this section. Use end-of-chapter problems 40–46, and 48.

V. Properties of Magnetic Materials

Section 17.8 describes the properties of different types of magnetic materials. In Observational Experiment Table 17.6, experiments lead students to three different types of materials that behave differently in an external magnetic field—so-called diamagnetic materials, paramagnetic materials, and ferromagnetic materials. Each type of material is described at a microscopic level.

18

Electromagnetic Induction

In Chapter 17, students learned that an electric current produces a magnetic field. This discovery in the 1800s led physicists to think that a magnetic field should be able to produce an electric current. In this chapter, students reproduce historical experiments and test ideas that led to the discovery that magnetic fields can indeed produce electric currents. The chapter is broken into four parts, starting with qualitative analysis and ending with more quantitative applications:

I. *Observe patterns in experiments to qualitatively develop the idea of electromagnetic induction and relate induction to changing magnetic flux*
II. *Develop Lenz's law and Faraday's law*
III. *Adapt the general problem-solving strategy to problems involving electromagnetic induction and apply the rules developed to analyze some important applications of electromagnetic induction*
IV. *Develop a deeper explanation for electromagnetic induction and see how it fits into the electricity and magnetism ideas developed in Chapters 14–17*

Chapter subject matter	**Related textbook section**	**ALG activities**	**End-of-chapter questions and problems**	**Videos**
Observe patterns in experiments to qualitatively develop the idea of electromagnetic induction and relate induction to changing magnetic flux	18.1, 18.2	18.1.1, 18.1.2, 18.1.5, 18.4.1	Questions 1, 2, 10 Problems 1, 3–7, 9, 10, 12	18.1, 18.2

Develop Lenz's law and Faraday's law	18.3, 18.4	18.1.6, 18.2.1, 18.2.2, 18.4.2–18.4.4	Questions 4–8, 21 Problems 13, 14, 17–20	18.3
Adapt the general problem-solving strategy to problems involving electromagnetic induction and apply the rules developed to analyze some important applications of electromagnetic induction	18.5–18.7, 18.9	18.3.2, 18.3.3, 18.4.5–18.4.10	Questions 9, 11, 12 Problems 17, 18, 20, 21, 23, 25–30, 32, 33–36, 38, 41,45, 46 50, 52, 59, 61	
Develop a deeper explanation for electromagnetic induction and see how it fits into the electricity and magnetism ideas developed in Chapters 14–17	18.10			

I. Observe Patterns in Experiments to Qualitatively Develop the Idea of Electromagnetic Induction and Relate Induction to Changing Magnetic Flux

The opening passage of Chapter 18 briefly describes transcranial magnetic stimulation (TMS), a method to induce an electric current in a person's brain by using electric current in a small coil placed on the scalp—completely noninvasive. How does this method work? To answer this question, students might start by observing and discussing experiments such as the textbook's Observational Experiment Table 18.1 or by doing Active Learning Guide (ALG) activities 18.1.1 and 18.1.2 in a lab. The goal of those activities is to devise a rule describing when a current can be induced in a circuit that does not have a battery. However, if your students have been designing experiments in the lab, you can make the task even more open-ended by turning this activity into a design lab. Give your students a magnet and a coil connected to a galvanometer and ask them to figure out how to make the current in the coil without any battery, just using a magnet. It might take a while for the students to accidentally find out that moving the magnet perpendicular to the coil creates the current in the coil. You cannot overestimate the joy that students experience when this happens!

Alternatively, if you think that your students are not ready for such open-ended exercises, you can proceed either with the ALG or textbook activities in which students look for patterns in a variety of experiments involving a bar magnet, a coil, and a galvanometer. What seems to be necessary in order to get a current in the coil? Most students immediately come up with this rule: when the magnet moves with respect to the coil, there is a current induced in the coil. They can test this rule in ALG activity 18.1.2.

It is important that when students make predictions, they actually use the rule they are testing. Sometimes students come up with another rule: the changing number of magnetic field lines through the coil leads to the current. Testing Experiment Table 18.2 provides experiments to test both rules. We suggest that you let your students make predictions by working together before observing the testing experiments and then reason about both rules. They can go back to the transcranial stimulation and realize that the first rule is inconsistent with the TMS method. As a result of multiple experiments, the second rule should be the one to survive. Students can use it to answer Conceptual Exercise 18.1. The textbook shows how to use this rule to explain how a dynamic microphone and a seismometer work. Students can work on end-of-chapter questions 1 and 2 and problems 1 and 3–7.

After students devise a qualitative rule, the next step is to find what determines the magnitude of the induced current. You can either proceed with ALG activity 18.1.5 or textbook Section 18.2, which describes the experiments indicating that three physical quantities that change are important for the number of $\vec{B}$ field lines, whose change is responsible for the induced current: the magnitude of the $\vec{B}$ field, the coil area A, and the orientation θ of the coil relative to the $\vec{B}$ field. Those quantities lead to a definition of magnetic flux Φ. ALG activity 18.4.1 helps students practice the definition. Students find flux a fairly difficult concept. It may help to make an analogy to a more familiar example such as collecting rain in a rectangular box. In this example, the relative orientation between the box and the rain affects how much rain is collected. Likewise, students can think of the loop as "collecting" field lines. To correctly account for how many $\vec{B}$ field lines pass through the loop, we need to consider both the area of the loop *and* its orientation relative to those field lines.

It is important to help students understand that flux itself does not cause an induced electric current—a change in flux does. The more quickly the flux changes, the greater is the induced current. The magnitude of the induced current also depends on the number of turns in a coil. Note that the term flux is confusing to the students—in everyday life, the word flux means change; therefore a discussion of the "physics" meaning of the word flux is crucial here. End-of-chapter question 10 and problems 9, 10, and 12 can be used here.

II. Develop Lenz's Law and Faraday's Law

The next step in students' investigation of electromagnetic induction is to develop a rule for the direction of the induced current. They can do so directly by experimenting with the coil connected to a galvanometer and a magnet, but we find that the experiment is too complicated for the students to keep track of all variables. They can work with the material in textbook Section 18.3, Figure 18.18. Alternatively, ALG activity 18.1.6 is clean enough for the students to see the pattern.

Students find that the direction of $\vec{B}_{in}$ is such that it always opposes the changes in the external flux—Lenz's law. This is a difficult concept for students to develop, especially for cases where the magnitude of the $\vec{B}_{ex}$ external field is decreasing, thus leading to $\vec{B}_{in}$ in the same direction. Our best advice is to give them a lot of practice. The textbook section *Reasoning Skill: Determining the Direction of an Induced Current* should receive extra attention if you want students to be able to apply Lenz's law. Students can work with ALG activity 18.2.1 and with Conceptual Exercise 18.3. Note eddy currents are introduced at the end of Section 18.3; this topic is a very useful application of Lenz's law. We use it to explain coin sorters and braking systems for vehicles. You can use end-of-chapter questions 4–8, and 21 and problems 13 and 14 to help students practice qualitative reasoning for electromagnetic induction.

After students have investigated the phenomenon of electromagnetic induction qualitatively, it is time for the quantitative aspect. Observational Experiment Table 18.3 in Section 18.4 provides students with the data that allow them to connect that the magnitude of the induced current depends on the time interval that the external magnetic flux changes (the shorter the time interval, the greater the induced current). ALG activity 18.2.2 helps solidify this connection. However, those observations are not enough to write Faraday's law. Moreover, Faraday's law does not have current; it is formulated in terms of emf. It is important to discuss this issue. Students often talk about potential difference or voltage when discussing Faraday's law. This vernacular is incorrect. Changing flux induces circulating or curl electric field that causes an induced current in the coil (students encounter this at the end of the chapter). This field can do nonzero work moving electric charges inside the coil along a closed loop (we know that this is true, because the loop gets warm). This means the field is nonconservative, unlike the electric field in electrostatics, which was conservative. Practically, this means that it is ambiguous to talk about the potential difference between two points in this field. To quantitatively characterize the work done by this field, use the quantity of emf, which has a value that depends only on how quickly the external flux is changing. The potential difference between points of the loop should not be confused with the emf generated by the changing magnetic field. To help students construct Faraday's law

$$\varepsilon_{in} = N\left|\frac{\Delta\Phi}{\Delta t}\right| \text{T}$$

we suggest that students first work with ALG activity 18.3.1 and then read Section 18.4 in the textbook, especially the text related to Figure 18.14. Note that the emf in these activities is not measured but is inferred from the measurements of the induced current (possible with the ammeter) and resistance of the coil in which the current is induced. Students can proceed to ALG activities 18.4.2–18.4.4 to apply the law to simple situations. End-of-chapter problems 17–20 provide more practice.

III. Adapt the General Problem-Solving Strategy to Problems Involving Electromagnetic Induction and Apply the Rules Developed to Analyze Some Important Applications of Electromagnetic Induction

Example 18.5 in Section 18.5 shows how to adapt the textbook's general problem-solving procedure to electromagnetic induction problems. After students work through examples in this section, they can do end-of-chapter question 12, problems 17, 18, 33–35 and ALG activities 18.4.5–18.4.7. Note that changes in $\vec{B}_{ex}$, A, and coil orientation θ relative to the $\vec{B}$ field can each cause an induced emf. Examples of each changing quantity inducing an emf are illustrated in the next three sections.

Before starting these applications it is good to review the math idea that nonchanging quantities are like constants and can be moved outside the change symbols. For example, if only B is changing, Faraday's law becomes:

$$\varepsilon_{in} = N\left|\frac{\Delta[BA\cos\theta]}{\Delta t}\right| = N\left|A\cos\theta\frac{\Delta B}{\Delta t}\right|$$

Example 18.6 in Section 18.6 illustrates the analysis of how a changing magnetic field causes an induced emf in the case of the transcranial magnetic stimulation procedure. Later, students can work on end-of chapter problems 20, 21, 25, 30, 32, 59, and 61.

The analysis of a changing area causing an induced emf is illustrated in Example 18.7 in Section 18.7. This example involves a metal axle with wheels on the end rolling on two tracks. The tracks are connected together on the opposite ends by a light bulb. A $\vec{B}$ field points down between the tracks. Faraday's law can be used to determine the induced emf between the ends of the tracks due to the increasing area between the light bulb, rails, and rolling axle. The *same emf* can be determined by considering charge separation that occurs in the axle due to the magnetic force exerted on the free electrons in the axle moving perpendicular to the $\vec{B}$ field. This is called motional emf. ALG activities 18.3.2 and 18.3.3 are designed to help students construct the concept of motional emf, so you might want to use these before students read the textbook section. Later, the students can try end-of-chapter question 9 and problems 23, 26–29, and 52 and ALG activities 18.4.8–18.4.10.

The analysis in Section 18.9 of the changing orientation of a coil relative to a $\vec{B}$ field leads to the derivation of the induced emf of a generator and the discussion of electric power plants. Students can try end-of-chapter problems 36, 38, 41, and 50. Although the book does not go into the details of wind turbines, you can assign students to investigate how wind turbines work and how they are similar to or different from the regular generators.

Section 18.9 uses Faraday's law to derive the effect of a relative number of input and output coils of a transformer on the input and output emfs. We apply the results of this derivation to see how to produce a 20,000-V spark in an automobile with only a 12-V battery. Students can work on question 11 and end-of-chapter problems 45 and 46.

A number of modern technologies that exploit the phenomenon of electromagnetic induction are not discussed in detail in the textbook. If you have more advanced students who need additional assignments or a capstone project, they can explore induction phenomena in everyday life. Some examples are how the magnetic strip on a credit card works, how electric guitar pickups work, magnetic levitation, and eddy currents.

IV. Develop a Deeper Explanation for Electromagnetic Induction and See How It Fits into the Electricity and Magnetism Ideas Developed in Chapters 14–17

So far, students have learned that if magnetic flux through a loop changes, there is an induced current in the loop. But they do not know the mechanism behind this process. Section 18.10 provides a deeper examination of why the phenomenon of electromagnetic induction exists (changing $\vec{B}$ field produces curl $\vec{E}$ field) and also summarizes the study of electricity and magnetism in Chapters 14–17. There is no parallel material in the ALG; thus we suggest that you have a discussion with your students in class, and that they read the section. They will need this material when they study electromagnetic waves in Chapter 24.

19

Vibrational Motion

This chapter starts a new unit: vibrations and waves (Chapters 19 and 20). Although both chapters involve only mechanical phenomena, they are separated by more than ten chapters from the rest of the mechanics chapters (Chapters 1–8). There are three reasons for this delay in the study of vibrations. First, these topics require more mathematical sophistication than those in the preceding chapters, and we wanted to delay this level of mathematics until as late as possible in the course. Second, we would like the modern physics wave part of the course to be as coherent as possible. To achieve this coherence, students need "fresh" understanding of waves. Third, returning to mechanics at this late stage in the course helps students refresh their memory of the tools that are necessary for the analysis of all physics phenomena—force diagrams and energy bar charts.

The main goal of this chapter is to help students learn a new kind of motion—vibrational motion—and a new model of motion—simple harmonic motion. Specifically we want them to learn how to analyze vibrational motion using motion, forces, and energy approaches. We also want them to learn the mathematical details of simple harmonic motion as a model of real motion. The chapter is broken into five parts, starting with qualitative analysis and ending with more quantitative applications. For each part, we describe instructional sequences, ideas and activities that can be used in labs, and lecture and problem-solving recitations. We also provide brief discussions of the motivation for using these activities.

I. *Qualitative description of vibrational motion*
II. *Describing vibration using kinematics, forces, and energy*
III. *Applying the same techniques to a simple pendulum*
IV. *Developing the skills to analyze vibrational motion*
V. *Including friction and driving force in vibrational motion*

Chapter subject matter	Related textbook section	ALG activities	End-of-chapter questions and problems	Videos
Qualitative description of vibrational motion	19.1	19.1.2, 19.1.3, 19.2.1, 19.2.2, 19.2.4	Questions 2–4	
Describing vibration using kinematics, forces, and energy	19.3–19.5	19.3.1, 19.3.2, 19.3.4, 19.4.1, 19.4.2, 19.4.5	Questions 5–9 Problems 10, 13, 16, 20, 22–24, 26–30, 32, 34, 65, 68	19.5
Applying the same techniques to a simple pendulum	19.6, 19.7	19.2.4, 19.3.5, 19.3.6	Problems 35, 37, 38, 40, 41, 49	
Developing the skills to analyze vibrational motion	19.7–19.10	19.4.6–19.4.12	Problems 45, 46, 48–50, 61, 62, 64, 69	
Including friction and driving force in vibrational motion	19.8, 19.9		Problems 52, 56, 58, 60	

I. Qualitative Description of Vibrational Motion

We suggest that students first observe different examples of vibrational motion to identify common features of this phenomenon. They can use objects attached to springs, pendulums, and any other vibrating systems. The experiments are described in Observational Experiment Table 19.1 and Active Learning Guide (ALG) activity 19.1.1. If you are starting in lecture, you can let them observe the experiments and then answer the ALG questions. Textbook Table 19.1 is designed to guide you in helping your students focus on important features of this new type of motion: the equilibrium position where the vibrating object is at rest when undisturbed and the movement of the object when disturbed past equilibrium in two directions. Students also should find that some other object (like a spring), if moved away from the equilibrium position, exerts a force on the vibrating object that tends to return (restore) it to the equilibrium position. ALG activities 19.1.2 and 19.1.3 allow students to explain and test these new ideas.

The next step is to qualitatively analyze vibrational motion in more detail (ALG activities 19.2.1–19.2.2). We suggest that you start with the example of a cart attached to a horizontal spring, as this is the easiest case in which restoring force can be clearly identified. Note that it can be difficult to find a spring with a sufficiently low spring constant that will allow you to set up this apparatus for an actual demonstration. The work-around solution is to attach a partially stretched spring to each end of a dynamics cart, attaching those springs to the opposite ends of the dynamics track. However, this setup can be more confusing than enlightening to students. Perhaps it is better to let students imagine the physical situation from the diagram rather than trying to give them the actual apparatus. Likewise, an object attached to a vertical spring represents a more complex situation, and a pendulum is even more complex. When students represent the motion of the carts with motion diagrams, force diagrams, and bar charts, encourage them to place the representations for the same instances under each other so the pattern is easier to see.

ALG activities 19.2.1 and 19.2.2 are probably the two most important activities for students to build their understanding of vibrational motion. We recommend allowing students to spend a good chunk of time on them. If you can't afford lecture time, they could be done in recitation. After the students work through those representations on their own, they can read textbook Observational Experiment Table 19.2 for answers to the ALG activities. Note that after this analysis, you can define the physical quantities of the amplitude and period for the students, for by then they should have a pretty good understanding of the meanings. You can use end-of-chapter questions 2, 3, and 4 here. After students have analyzed the motion of a cart on a spring qualitatively, you can ask them to repeat this analysis for a pendulum (ALG activity 19.2.4) or follow the textbook and focus on the quantitative analysis of the cart-on-the-spring motion. After that is finished, go back to the pendulum analysis.

II. Describing Vibration Using Kinematics, Forces, and Energy

Textbook Sections 19.3–19.5 and ALG Section 19.3 help develop the strategies needed to describe vibrational motion quantitatively. Students start with an observational experiment of the motion of an object hanging from a spring using a motion detector. In this way, the shapes of the position, velocity, and acceleration graphs are immediately established as an observation fact. This can be done either in lab or as a lecture demonstration. ALG activity 19.3.1 is the key activity here. If the learning cycle starts in lab, remove the graphs and only use the accompanying questions. ALG activity 19.3.1 asks students to focus on whether the three graphs are consistent with each other and whether they are consistent with motion and force diagrams constructed earlier.

It is very important that students work through these consistency checks. If they rush or are rushed through these elementary steps, they will fail to see the connections between all their representations (pictorial, graphical, and mathematical). The end result is a weak understanding that manifests itself as rote equation matching instead of deep and thoughtful analysis when students have to solve difficult problems.

Next, students need to establish the mathematical equations that describe the three graphs they have observed. ALG activity 19.3.2 asks students to do this without much assistance. Very few students will be able to do this without help; thus it is better to use this activity in conjunction with the subsection "Mathematical Description of Position as a Function of Time" in Section 19.3. Note here the difference between vibrational motion as a physical phenomenon and simple harmonic motion (SHM) as a *model* of such motion.

Students can practice the mathematics in textbook Example 19.2 and then work with ALG activities 19.4.1 and 19.4.2, textbook Quantitative Exercise 19.3 (an Equation Jeopardy problem that provides an exercise for interpreting a kinematics vibrational motion equation), and textbook end-of-chapter questions 5–8 and problems 10, 13, and 16.

The next step is to find out what variables the period of vibrational motion of an object attached to a spring depends on. The problem with simply deriving the relationship $T = 2\pi \sqrt{m/k}$ from Newton's second law is that it doesn't allow students to test the idea that amplitude might affect the period. The most effective approach is to ask students to briefly brainstorm what variables they think affect the period and whether each variable will make the period longer or shorter. Let them conduct the testing experiments in ALG activity 19.3.4 to test whether those variables affect the period as they suggested. (Alternatively, you can have the experiments ready to run as lecture demonstrations.) In this way, students *disprove* for themselves that amplitude matters. This helps convince them more than pointing to the equation for the period where there is no amplitude. Textbook Section 19.4 shows students a path to the mathematical relation between k, m, and T using Newton's second law and the mathematical expressions for $x(t)$ and $a(t)$. Students can work on textbook end-of-chapter question 9 and problems 20, 22–24, and 65.

In textbook Section 19.5, students apply the ideas of work and energy in the analysis of vibrational motion. Table 19.4 has a summary of the potential energy, the kinetic energy, and the total energy of a cart-spring system at different times during one cycle of vibration. Students learn how to develop an expression for the energy of this system at different times. This expression leads to a useful equation relating the cart's maximum speed to the amplitude of vibration. All of the work energy ideas are used in Example 19.5 to answer many questions about the cart-spring system. ALG activity 19.4.5 and textbook end-of-chapter problems 26–30, 32, 34, and 68 can be used with students in lectures or recitations.

III. Applying the Same Techniques to a Simple Pendulum

The same approach, from observations and qualitative analysis to the explanations and quantitative analysis, can be applied to a pendulum. We mostly focus on the model of a real pendulum, the simple pendulum, in which the bob is considered a point-like object, the string does not stretch, and the amplitude of vibrations is small.

The motion and force analyses of the simple pendulum are more complicated than those of an object attached to a spring as the sum of the forces exerted on the pendulum bob (force exerted by the string and by Earth) is not pointed toward the equilibrium position. To analyze the motion of the pendulum, it is beneficial to set up a new coordinate system, with the radial axis and the tangential axis. The restoring force in the case of the pendulum is the tangential component of the net force. This component always points toward the equilibrium position and is responsible for the change in the velocity vector. The radial component of the net force makes the bob move in an arc and is responsible for the change in the direction of the velocity vector. Students conduct the qualitative analysis of the pendulum's motion in ALG activity 19.2.4. They will require considerable help with this activity. If they get stuck, they can check their work with textbook Table 19.5. ALG activities 19.3.5 and 19.3.6 can be done in a lab, where students come up with and test the expression for the period of the pendulum.

In the textbook (Section 19.6), they first read Observational Experiment Table 19.5, which shows how to represent the vibrational motion of a simple pendulum in multiple ways: a motion diagram, force diagrams, and gravitational potential and kinetic energies. Table 19.6 provides data related to the effect of a pendulum string length, the amplitude of vibration, and the pendulum bob mass on the period and frequency of the pendulum. Analysis of the data should help students see that the period depends only on the length of the string. A derivation of the period and frequency of a pendulum is consistent with this outcome. The textbook applies the pendulum analysis to the swinging frequency of a leg and the dependence of leg length on the number of steps per unit time. Conceptual Exercise 19.7 shows how to do a complete energy analysis of the motion of the pendulum. Students can try end-of-chapter problems 35, 37, 38, 40, 41, and 49.

IV. Developing the Skills to Analyze Vibrational Motion

We use a NASA body mass measurement system in Example 19.8 in Section 19.7 to illustrate how to adapt the book's general problem-solving methods to vibrational motion problems. We apply the method to another problem, involving a skier who runs into and attaches to a padded cart with a spring on the other side. The skier and cart undergo vibrational motion at the end of the ski run. After this section, students can work with ALG activities 19.4.6–19.4.10. If you have lab time, perform experiments described in ALG activities 19.4.11 and 19.4.12.

Students can read textbook Section 19.10, in which the vibrational motion concepts are applied to understanding Example 19.11 on the vibration of CO_2 molecules in the atmosphere and the way the absorption of infrared radiation from Earth contributes to greenhouse warming. This is followed by analysis of inverse bungee jumping in Example 19.12. Students can then try end-of-chapter problems 45, 46, 48–50, 61, 62, 64, and 69.

V. Including Friction and Driving Force in Vibrational Motion

Section 19.8 is dedicated to the damping of vibrating systems (weakly damped, critically damped, and over-damped oscillators). We use examples of damped oscillations such as automobile shock absorbers (critically damped) and a spider's web (weakly damped).

Section 19.9 introduces students to forced vibrations through Observational Experiment Table 19.6. By analyzing the data in the table, students should come to the following conclusions: the amplitude of forced vibrations increases when the frequency and period of the application of the external force are the same as the natural frequency and period of the vibrating system. The explanation for this pattern comes from the energy analysis. When those two frequencies are the same, the external force exerted on the vibrating system does positive work on it, and the energy of the system increases. The idea is then tested in a simple experiment with several pendulums of different lengths hanging from a sagging horizontal cord. This particular experimental setup is easy to make, and we strongly recommend that you do. It allows students to analyze forced vibrations deeply and develop confidence in their ideas. Real-world examples of forced vibrations include a marching band that caused a bridge to collapse, breaking a wine glass with the correct frequency sound, and vibrations of the Tacoma Narrows Bridge. Students can work on end-of-chapter problems 52, 56, 58, and 60.

20

Mechanical Waves

Chapter 19, on vibrational motion, laid a foundation for the study of mechanical waves in this chapter. In Chapter 19, students learned to describe and explain the vibrational of one point-like object. In this chapter students will learn how vibrations originated at one location spread through the medium. Mathematically speaking, instead of describing the motion of an object using a sinusoidal function of one variable—time—they will learn how to describe motion using a sinusoidal function of two variables, time and the position of the vibrating object. The chapter is broken into six parts:

I. *A qualitative analysis and kinematics description of waves*
II. *A dynamics and work-energy analysis of waves*
III. *Wave interference*
IV. *The application of these ideas to sound waves*
V. *Standing waves on string instruments and in pipes*
VI. *The Doppler effect for sound*

For each part, we suggest activities that can be used in a lab, lecture, and recitations to help students develop and test these ideas. We also provide brief discussions of the motivations for using these activities.

Chapter subject matter	Related textbook section	ALG activities	End-of-chapter questions and problems	Videos
A qualitative analysis and kinematics description of waves	20.1, 20.2	20.1.1–20.1.3, 20.2.1–20.2.5, 20.3.1, 20.3.2	Questions 1–7 Problems 5–10, 13, 14	20.1

A dynamics and work-energy analysis of waves	20.3, 20.4	20.1.4, 20.3.3, 20.3.4	Question 8 Problems 15–18, 22–25, 53	20.2
Wave interference	20.5, 20.6		Problems 27–30, 34, 35, 39	20.5
Application of these ideas to sound waves	20.7, 20.8		Problems 45–47, 49	
Standing waves on string instruments and in pipes	20.9, 20.10	20.3.5–20.3.8, 20.4.4–20.4.8	Problems 50–54, 56, 59–62	20.7
Constructing and applying the Doppler effect for sound	20.11	20.1.7–20.1.9, 20.3.9, 20.4.9	Problems 65–69, 71, 77	

I. A Qualitative Analysis and Kinematics Description of Waves

Students start to learn wave motion with the motion of nonrepeating pulses. You can use Active Learning Guide (ALG) activities 20.1.1 and 20.1.2 to help students conduct initial observations of wave motion. These observations help students to see the difference between transverse and longitudinal pulses, their propagation in space, and indirectly the independence of the wave speed on the frequency of the wave. It is best if students actually perform the experiments described in the ALG activities and observe the motion of the individual Slinky coils, the generated pulse, and the reflected pulse. If it is not possible for the students to conduct the experiments themselves, you can demonstrate the ALG experiments or experiments described in Section 20.1, Observational Experiment Table 20.1.

When students observe pulses traveling on a string (or a Slinky), focus their attention on the fact that the disturbance moves along the string (or a Slinky), but a ribbon on the string (or a marked Slinky coil) moves perpendicular to the string as the pulse passes but does not travel along the string. Students tend to think that the material through which a wave disturbance travels actually moves in the same direction—perhaps because ocean waves push us toward the shore. Give students time to explore the possibility that the harder you shake the Slinky, the faster the wave moves. In our experience, most students haven't distinguished between frequency and amplitude yet. They suspect that the more "oomph" you put into shaking the Slinky, the faster the pulse will move. A bigger "oomph" is some combination of a quicker hand movement and larger amplitude. Students can explore this idea and refute it for themselves through careful experimentation with the Slinky.

ALG activity 20.1.3 moves students from a pulse to a wave. If you have a body of water near by, it is worth taking students outside to perform this activity; if not, a simple wave tank will do. Just make sure you put some cloth on the outside to cancel the reflected waves. Textbook Section 20.1 introduces students to wave fronts and different types of mechanical waves—water waves and sound waves.

After students explore pulse motion qualitatively and transition to wave motion at the end of Section 20.1, they can proceed to working with section 20.2, which helps them define the physical quantities that describe wave motion: period, frequency, amplitude, and propagation speed. The quantity of the wavelength appears after students see how to construct a mathematical description of a sinusoidal wave. We suggest that you examine carefully the steps that lead to the wave function $y(x,t) = A\cos[(2\pi/T)(t - x/v)]$ and the subsequent introduction of the wavelength.

We first construct a function for the position as a function of time for one point in the medium (we choose this point to be the vibrating source). Then we write the time function describing the vibration of a point that is x meters away from the source. This function is similar, but we need to take into account that vibrations arrive to this point with a time delay equal to $\frac{x}{v}$. Thus we can write the function $y(t)$ for every point of the medium as

$$A\cos[\frac{2\pi}{T}(t - \frac{x}{v})] = A\cos[\frac{2\pi}{T}t - \frac{2\pi}{T}\frac{x}{v})],$$

which means that we have the function of two variables—time and position, $y(x,t)$. The new wave equation allows us to find the points in the medium that always have the same displacement at the same clock reading, the points that vibrate in phase. To find them, we set $[(2\pi)/T](x/v) = 2\pi n$ where n is any integer. Therefore the distance between those points is $x = nTv$. The closest of those points ($n = 1$) are said to be separated by a distance called the wavelength. Thus we can define the cause-effect relation for the wavelength $\lambda = Tv = \frac{v}{f}$. This approach helps students understand that the wavelength depends on the motion of the source (period of the wave) and the properties of the medium (wave speed).

A common way of writing the same equation as $v = f\lambda$ does not allow students to see this cause-effect relationship, and unnecessary confusion results. To understand wavelength operationally, it helps students to think of it as the distance the wave travels in the medium in the time of one period of the source oscillation. It is useful to have students summarize and organize the large number of new physical quantities that they have discovered and the relationships among them. They need to realize that frequency and period depend on the behavior of the source. Wave speed depends only on properties of the medium in which it travels. Wavelength is determined both by the source *and* by the medium in which the wave travels. Having students organize their ideas at this point serves as an excellent foundation for the more difficult wave topics that are still to come.

Students can work on textbook Example 20.1, an Equation Jeopardy problem in which students learn to tell everything they can about a wave whose wave equation is known. After this example they can work on ALG activities 20.2.1–20.5, 20.3.1, 20.3.2, and end-of-chapter questions 1–7 and problems 5–10, 13, and 14.

II. A Dynamics and Work-Energy Analysis of Waves

After students have learned to construct the function that describes the motion of each point in a wave, the next step is to investigate what physical quantities affect wave speed. A conceptual activity that is useful to start with is ALG activity 20.1.4, and then students can proceed to ALG activities 20.3.3 and 20.3.4. The latter two activities provide data concerning the speed of wave propagation along several strings. The data analysis allows students to construct the cause-effect relationship that connects the speed of the wave to the properties of the medium. They do not need equipment to do those activities, so you can use them in a lecture setting or a problem-solving session.

A similar setup is described in the textbook. Table 20.2 in Section 20.3 provides the data and the analysis showing how A, f, and the force you exert pulling on the end of the string affect the speed v of a wave on the string. Force is the only one of these three quantities that affects the wave speed. Other experiments indicate that the mass per unit length of the string also affects the wave speed. These ideas lead to an expression for the wave speed. The expression is tested with the experiment in Table 20.3. Since the wave speed depends only on properties of the medium and the wave frequency depends only on the source vibration frequency, the wavelength depends on the wave speed and the frequency. Students can work on ALG activity 20.3.4 and end-of-chapter question 8 and problems 15–18, and 53.

In Section 20.4, students analyze single wave pulses produced in two-and three-dimensional media. The energy of the pulse spreads over greater surface areas for each case. Thus, the amplitude of the wave decreases as it spreads from the source of the wave. This leads to the introduction of a new quantity, the wave intensity, which is used later in this chapter and in subsequent chapters. You can assign end-of-chapter problems 22–25 here.

III. Wave Interference

Textbook Section 20.5 describes experiments with wave pulses that are partially reflected and partially transmitted if passing from one medium to another medium with different density (a mass-like quantity) or a different coupling of the particles in the medium (a force-like quantity). Students can observe these experiments in lecture to start thinking about the impedance of a medium and impedance matching to reduce the reflection of waves at the boundary of different media. We provide biological examples of this important idea. Use end-of-chapter problems 27–30.

To construct the principle of superposition, we start with an example. Textbook Section 20.6 describes experiments with two upright, oppositely traveling pulses passing through each other. It is best if you perform these experiments as observational demos in a lecture setting or let students perform them in a lab. If you ask students to explain what they observed, some will suggest that the two pulses passed through each other, but others will suggest that the pulses bounced off of each other and were reflected back. You can use the second experiment (one upright, one inverted pulse) to test both of these ideas. Ask students to predict what they will see based on each idea (passing through and bouncing back) before you run the second experiment. Once it is established that the two pulses pass through each other, students need to observe how the pulses add together when they're on top of each other.

We then apply this idea of pulses adding or subtracting to waves created in swimming pool water by two synchronously vibrating beach balls. Looking along a line that is equidistant from the two vibrating beach balls, one observes a resultant wave that has twice the amplitude of a single wave. Students should be able to construct the superposition principle analyzing these simple observations. This analysis is very important for helping students understand Young's double slit interference experiment, which they will encounter later in wave optics.

In the same section, Section 20.6, you will see how the textbook's general problem-solving strategy is adapted to problems involving wave motion. Example 20.4 shows the general steps (on the left side of a problem-solving table) and their application to the problem (on the right side). The last subsection in Section 20.6 is dedicated to Huygens principle. We start with an analysis of an imaginary observational experiment that leads to the Huygens "idea." The idea is then tested in Testing Experiment Table 20.5. Students can work on end-of-chapter problems 34, 35, and 39.

IV. The Application of These Ideas to Sound Waves

Since students encountered sound in Section 20.1, Section 20.7 focuses primarily on the physiological impression related to the loudness of sound. The intensity of sound is a physical measure of the variation of pressure of sound waves about atmospheric pressure. However, our impression of sound loudness is measured by a quantity called intensity level—defined in this section and applied in Quantitative Example 20.6 to the sound in a busy classroom.

Section 20.8 deals with the frequency of sound, the subjective impression of the pitch of a sound, and complex sounds, which are in part related to the quality of a sound. A complex sound, which consists of multiple frequencies of single-frequency sound waves heard simultaneously, is analyzed in terms of a waveform and a frequency spectrum. The waveforms from musical instruments and the corresponding frequency spectra are first introduced here. A very nice quantitative example of a complex wave is the beats and beat frequency produced by two waves of nearly the same frequency. Students in lectures or recitations can try end-of-chapter problems 45, 46, 47, and 49.

V. Standing Waves on String Instruments and in Pipes

Observational Experimental Table 20.7 in Section 20.9 helps students understand how the first standing wave vibration on a string is formed. The key elements to helping students understand how standing waves are formed are that the wave is being reflected at each boundary and that the harmonic motion of the source needs to be synchronized with the time it takes for the wave to move back and forth on the string. Once students understand these elements, they can work out the mathematical relationship for standing waves. They test the result by predicting the first standing wave frequency of the D string on a banjo (Testing Experiment Table 20.8). Students can then work on ALG activity 20.3.5 and end-of-chapter problems 50–54 and 56.

The process is repeated in Section 20.10 for the first standing wave in an open-open pipe. Then we discuss the standing wave frequencies of an open-closed pipe—this case is more complicated because a wave has to complete two round-trips, so it is reinforced constructively to produce the fundamental frequency. The standing wave frequencies of various musical instruments are related to the open-open and open-closed pipe frequencies. Students can work on ALG activities 20.4.4–20.4.8 and end-of-chapter problems 59–62. ALG activities 20.3.6–20.3.8 are examples of possible lab activities at the end of this chapter's standing wave subunit.

VI. Constructing and Applying the Doppler Effect for Sound

Earlier in the chapter, the frequency of observed waves equaled the frequency of the source. To start students' exploration of the Doppler effect, we suggest that you have students perform or observe experiments described in Observational Experiment Table 20.9 in Section 20.11.

Students observe that the frequency of an observed wave is greater than the frequency of the source of the wave if the relative motion of the source and observer is toward each other; the observed frequency is less if the source and observer are moving apart. They can work on ALG activities 20.1.7–20.1.9 to construct a conceptual understanding of the Doppler effect.

You can repeat the textbook derivation for the frequency change with the source moving relative to the medium through which the wave travels and with the observer moving relative to the medium. Combining these two expressions leads to the Doppler effect equation for sound. If you follow the derivation, the students will build this concept using their own observations.

Students can work on ALG activity 20.3.9, which encourages them to make sense of the equation. The Doppler equation with $\pm$ on the top and $\mp$ on the bottom can be confusing to use. We provide the rules, but a good check is to recall the outcomes of the Table 20.9 experiments and choose the plus or minus sign that matches the situation being addressed. We use the Doppler equation to show one method to measure blood speed (students can work on ALG activity 20.4.9 and read the text) and the changing frequency of a buzzer moving in a circle. Students can then work on end-of-chapter problems 65–69, 71, and 77. In lectures, it is sometimes fun to take a multipart problem like Problem 66 and have one-fourth of the class work on Part (a), one-fourth work on Part (b), and so forth.

21

Reflection and Refraction

In this chapter, we start the first of four sequential chapters involving light. The focus of this chapter is on light emission and light propagation in different media. Students learn about two models explaining the behavior of light. In the first model, light is analogous to a stream of fast-moving bullets, and in the second, light is analogous to a wave. The chapter is broken into four parts:

I. *Qualitative analysis of light propagation and emission*
II. *Reflection, refraction, and total reflection of light*
III. *Skills for analyzing light reflection and refraction and applications*
IV. *Models of the nature of light*

For each part, we describe activities that you can use in labs, lectures, and problem-solving sessions to help students acquire these ideas. We also provide brief discussions of the motivations for using these activities.

Chapter subject matter	**Related textbook section**	**ALG activities**	**End-of-chapter questions and problems**	**Videos**
Qualitative analysis of light propagation and emission	21.1	21.1.1–21.1.6, 21.2.1, 21.2.2	Questions 2–5 Problems 1, 3, 5, 7	21.1, 21.2
Reflection, refraction, and total reflection of light	21.2–21.4	21.1.7–21.1.9, 21.2.3, 21.2.5, 21.2.6, 21.3.1–21.3.5, 21.4.1–21.4.3	Questions 8, 11 Problems 10, 11, 15, 18–23, 25–27, 29, 30, 32–35, 38	21.4

Skills for analyzing light reflection and refraction and applications	21.5, 21.6	21.4.5–21.4.11	Questions 9, 10 Problems 30, 42, 44–52, 54, 56, 60	
Models of the nature of light	21.7	21.1.10, 21.1.13	Problems 45–47, 49	

I. A Qualitative Analysis of Light Propagation and Emission

In our experience, and based on research on students' understanding of optics, many difficulties that students have with optics may be traced back to inadequately developed models of the two most basic light phenomena: how light is emitted from a source or reflected off of an object, and the role of the human eye in perceiving light phenomena. We believe that instructors should pay extra attention to these foundational ideas. The question "How do we see things?" is a nontrivial one for many students. First we need a source of light, then this light has to reach the object we want to see, and then light bounces off it and reaches our eyes. However, in ancient times people thought that their eyes emitted light rays that reached the objects, wrapped around them, and returned to their eyes, bringing them information about the object. Many people still have this idea in some form, and thus they often believe that if we sit in a dark room for a long time we will eventually be able to see. Active Learning Guide (ALG) activity 21.1.1 addresses this issue. The ideal situation is if you have a completely dark room, where you can let your students sit for a while and then ask them if they see anything. This experiment works only if the room is completely dark, but it is extremely powerful when it works. Ask students to explain why they cannot see anything. To explain the outcome of this experiment, students need to come up with the idea that a source of light is needed to be able to see objects.

The next step is to help students construct two ideas: (1) light travels in straight lines in the same medium, and (2) one cannot see light from a source unless this light is reflected off some object and reaches the eyes of the observer. Students can complete ALG activity 21.1.2 (the same activity is described in textbook Table 21.1). Students observe and analyze the experiments involving a laser beam. The experiments can be easily and quickly reproduced in large or small classrooms. Note here that a laser is an artificially made source of light that sends a very narrow parallel beam of light. When there are no obstacles, such as chalk dust, the beam itself is not seen but only the spot on the wall that the beam hits. These simple experiments help students construct the idea that for us to see something, light has to bounce off it and reach the observer's eyes.

The most important idea that students need to construct is a model of how light is emitted by a source. For this, students need a concept of a ray of light. We introduce it as an arrow that represents the direction that light travels (Section 21.1).

The key question that we pose to students is, does each point of an extended light source emit one ray or multiple rays? To answer this question, students are asked to test two models, one model with one ray from each point (rather like a child's depiction of the Sun) and one with multiple rays from each point. If you have a lab period for this, then students can work on ALG activity 21.1.3. If you do this material in a lecture setting, then the same activity can be done with students working in groups of two coming up with testing experiments and with you performing them. Make sure you have a piece of foil handy to cover the bulb, as one of the most common experiments requires it. Some possible experiments are described in the textbook's Testing Experiment Table 21.2. Testing experiments reject the one-ray model, and the multiple-ray model remains.

Give students lots of time to draw ray diagrams in order to make predictions for the outcomes of the different experiments using the two different models. This is likely the first time they are drawing ray diagrams, so they may need the extra time. The next ALG activities (21.1.4–21.4.6) help students solidify their understanding of this concept. Students can do these in a lab or talk about them in a class discussion after observing the experiment.

If you are doing ALG activity 21.1.6 in a lecture setting (Conceptual Exercise 21.2 in the textbook), you will need to use a camera to capture the inverted flame of the candle on the screen. Alternatively, if you are in a room with windows that you covered for the first activity, you can ask your students to predict what will happen if you make a small hole in the shade. If they say that they will see street objects upside down on the opposite wall, they really understand the concept of multiple rays. To help students practice drawing ray diagrams and explain shadows, use ALG activities 21.2.1 and 21.2.2 and textbook questions 2–5 and problems 1, 3, 5, and 7.

It is critically important that students build a robust model of how light is emitted from an extended source because the concept that each point of a light-emitting object sends multiple rays is crucial later for drawing ray diagrams for mirrors and lenses. The time your students spend on these basic ideas will pay dividends later.

II. Reflection, Refraction, and Total Reflection of Light

If you are starting in a lecture setting, you can provide the students with the data presented in Observational Experiment Table 21.3 in Section 21.2 without them seeing the whole table so they can find the pattern on their own. If you start this section in a lab, students can do ALG activities 21.1.7 and 21.1.8 to construct and test the law of specular reflection. It is important to emphasize for students that the angles used are angles relative to the normal line and not relative to the surface. Conceptual Exercise 21.3 serves as a testing experiment for the law. ALG activity 21.2.5 provides good practice right away.

The book proceeds to a discussion of the contrast between specular and diffuse reflections. To help students learn this concept, you can first ask them to work on ALG activity 21.2.6 and read this discussion in the book. ALG 21.2.6 is an excellent opportunity for group discussion. It is critically important because students need to reconcile the ideas they developed earlier regarding diffuse reflection with the new phenomenon of specular reflection that they are currently studying. ALG activities 21.4.1 and 21.4.2 and end-of-chapter problems 10, 11, 15, 18, and 19 provide good practice.

The next topic is refraction. If you are starting in a lecture, you can show students the experiment described in ALG activity 21.1.9 and textbook Observational Experiment Table 21.4 in Section 21.3. Before students read this table, it is best if they observe and analyze the direction of travel of a narrow light beam partially reflected from an interface between two different media and the direction of that same beam when partially transmitted (refracted) into the second medium. These activities allow the students to construct the concept of refraction qualitatively. You may notice that we try to emphasize that there is always reflection *and* refraction at the boundary between different optical media. Too often the reflected rays are left out, causing students to develop unnecessary misunderstandings, such as thinking that there is no reflection when there is refraction.

To devise Snell's law, they can work through ALG activities 21.3.1 and 21.3.2 and then test their constructed rules by doing ALG activity 21.3.4 (parallel textbook Tables 21.5 and 21.6 provide angles of refraction for different angles of incidence). Analysis of the provided data leads to the introduction of the refractive indices of the media and to Snell's law. Example 21.5 uses Snell's law to determine the index of refraction of blood. You can assign ALG activities 21.2.3, 21.3.3, and 21.4.3 and textbook end-of-chapter question 8 and problems 20–23, 25–27, and 29–30. Note that it is very important here for students to draw the normal lines carefully.

The next step is to help students come up with the concept of an angle of the total internal reflection. As students have noted in the previous section, light bends away from the normal line when passing from an optically denser higher index of refraction material into an optically less dense lower index of refraction material. In ALG activity 21.3.5, students use their knowledge of refraction to predict what will happen to light traveling from glass to air. After students make predictions and then observe the experiment, they can read the explanation presented in textbook Section 21.4. Note biological examples of the application of this phenomenon at the end of this section. End-of-chapter question 11 and problems 32–35 and 38 are good for practice.

III. Skills for Analyzing Light Reflection and Refraction and Applications

In Section 21.5, students practice using ray diagrams to help their reasoning and quantitative problem-solving for processes involving reflection, refraction, and total internal reflection. The general problem-solving strategy of the textbook is adapted to such processes in Example 21.9, where the strategy is outlined on the left side of a table and applied to the example problem on the right side. An Equation Jeopardy worked example follows: students have to make sense of an equation that is the answer to an unknown problem. Students can then work on ALG activities 21.4.5–21.4.9 and textbook end-of-chapter problems 42, 44–52, 56, 60, and 30. One of the common difficulties that students experience here is drawing light rays coming from people's eyes as opposed to coming from an object. If you notice your students doing this, ask them where the object is that emits the light.

Textbook Section 21.6 includes the following four interesting and important applications of this chapter. Fiber optics has widespread use in medicine, communications, and other applications. The book first treats it quantitatively (Example 21.11) and then proceeds to the qualitative discussion. We next discuss the operation of prisms along with some of its applications. When students work with prisms, it is important that they draw normal lines carefully. Mirages are an interesting application of the refraction of light in air, whose temperature and index of refraction varies with the temperature. Finally, there is an extensive analysis of why the sky is blue when looking in most directions away from the Sun and why it is red at sunset. Students can work on end-of-chapter questions 9 and 10 and problem 54. Good laboratory activities at the end of this chapter are ALG activities 21.4.10 and 21.4.11.

IV. Models of the Nature of Light

Section 21.7 is dedicated to the explanations of the observed behavior of light. To explain the observed phenomena, scientists built analogical models using something familiar as a base for the analogy. Historically, there were two models (the particle and the wave model) that successfully explained light propagation, reflection, and refraction. However, the two models predict different changes in light speed when light passes from one medium to another. The wave model predicts a smaller speed, and the particle model predicts a larger speed when light transitions from a less dense to a more dense optical medium. At the time of the development of ideas of refraction, light speed could not be measured in different media, and consequently the refraction phenomenon did not eliminate either the wave or the particle model. We follow the same approach, leaving the question unresolved, and will return to the subject in later chapters. This section is where you can introduce the students to Huygens's principle and let them work through the details of using the wave model to explain refraction. We suggest that you start with ALG activities 21.1.10–21.1.13 (or similar activities) and then let students read the textbook. They can work on textbook end-of-chapter problems 45, 46, 47, and 49. Note that it is not necessary to introduce Huygens's principle at the end of the chapter. It works equally well if you weave this section in earlier when students are first discovering the phenomenon of refraction.

22

Mirrors and Lenses

Chapter 21 involved the study of reflection and refraction. In this chapter, we extend these ideas by studying the way in which mirrors and lenses form images of light from objects that reflect from the mirrors or pass through the lenses. Students will analyze experiments and test ideas involving image formation. The chapter is broken into five parts:

I. *Analysis of image formation by plane mirrors*
II. *Qualitative and quantitative analysis of image formation by curved mirrors*
III. *Qualitative and quantitative analysis of image formation by lenses*
IV. *The skills needed to solve mirror and lens problems, including the optics of the eye*
V. *Angular magnification, magnifying glasses, telescopes, and microscopes*

For each part, activities can be used in lecture and recitations to help students acquire these ideas. Brief discussions of the motivations for using these activities are provided.

Chapter subject matter	**Related textbook section**	**ALG activities**	**End-of-chapter questions and problems**
Analysis of image formation by plane mirrors	22.1	22.1.1, 22.1.2, 22.2.1–22.2.3	Questions 1–3
Qualitative and quantitative analysis of image formation by curved mirrors	22.2, 22.3	22.1.4–22.1.9, 22.2.4, 22.2.5, 22.2.7, 22.2.8, 22.2.10, 22.2.11, 22.3.1	Questions 4–6 Problems 8, 9, 14–23

Qualitative and quantitative analysis of image formation by lenses	22.4, 22.5	22.1.8, 22.1.10–22.1.12, 22.3.2, 22.3.3, 22.4.10	Questions 7–10, 12 Problems 26–30, 32, 33, 75, 76
Skills needed to solve more complex mirror and lens problems, including the optics of the eye, telescopes, and microscopes	22.6, 22.7	22.4.3–22.4.7, 22.4.9–22.4.15	Problems 34, 37, 38, 41–46, 50–56
Angular magnification, magnifying glasses, telescopes, and microscopes	22.8, 22.9	Problems 61–64, 67–69, 71–74, 77, 78	Problems 58–60

I. Analysis of Image Formation by Plane Mirrors

Students can analyze the ray diagrams for the plane mirror experiments in Observational Experiment Table 22.1 to develop a rule for the image location of an object in front of the mirror. Alternately, students can work through Active Learning Guide (ALG) activities 22.1.1, 22.1.2, and 22.2.1 if you begin this section in lab or lecture.

Note that students struggle with the concept of a virtual image, both in understanding its nature and in locating its perceived position. Work with students to help them understand that perceiving the position of an image is intimately tied into human binocular vision. The key idea is that we perceive an image from wherever the light rays appear to originate. Being able to locate the position of that image requires at least two rays coming from the same point of the object to reach the eye of the observer. ALG activities 22.1.1 and 22.1.2 are excellent supporting activities here.

The rule that the image is the same distance behind the mirror as the object is in front is tested by experiments in Testing Experiment Table 22.2. The tested rule is used to locate a tilted lamp in Conceptual Exercise 22.1. In Conceptual Exercise 22.2, students have to apply their understanding of ray diagrams and reflection to figure out the size of the smallest mirror that can be purchased in order to see their entire image in a mirror (a challenging activity). It is better to have students work though this activity on their own in recitations or lab. If you want to students to figure this out, they should first start with ALG activity 22.2.2, which asks students what happens to the size of an image in a plane mirror when the object is moved closer or farther away. ALG activity 22.2.3 challenges students to use ray diagrams to find the smallest mirror necessary to see the entire image of one's body. End-of-chapter questions 1–3 can be used with students in lectures or recitations. Students sometimes draw rays coming from the eyes of the observer as opposed to the object. Remind them to think about where the light rays start.

II. Qualitative and Quantitative Analysis of Image Formation by Curved Mirrors

Textbook Section 22.2 involves a qualitative analysis of image formation by curved mirrors in terms of principal rays, and Section 22.3 involves a quantitative analysis (the derivation of the mirror equation). Rays represent the direction of light travel from before to after reflection from a mirror. Rays are not real entities, just representations for the direction of light travel. We use the word beam for a narrow amount of light traveling from one place to another. To analyze concave mirrors, students can read Observational Experiment Table 22.3 in Section 22.2, where students see that parallel rays reflect from a concave mirror and converge through a single focal point. Students can also start with ALG activities 22.1.4, 22.1.6, 22.1.7, and 22.1.8. Through observation and testing, these activities help them construct the principal rays. Figure 22.6 provides a geometric proof that the distance from the focal point to the mirror is one-half the radius of the curvature of the mirror.

Students need to solidify their ideas and use them to understand how to find the location of the image formed by a concave mirror. Textbook Reasoning Skill 22.1 and ALG activities 22.2.4 and 22.2.5 are intended for this purpose. The skill box provides explicit instructions for determining the image distance from the mirror. The nature of images (real or virtual, upright or inverted, and enlarged or reduced in size compared to the object) is discussed in detail and illustrated using ray diagrams. ALG activity 22.2.8 is best used as a recitation or homework activity. In this activity, students draw ray diagrams to find the location of the image formed by a concave mirror for the three standard cases: $s > R$, $s < f < R$, and $s < f$. This activity is key for building their understanding of the behavior of concave mirrors. Once students have completed this activity they can work through textbook Conceptual Exercise 22.3, which illustrates the different object-image types.

You can follow a similar sequence with convex mirrors starting with ALG activities 22.1.5 and 22.1.9. Students can also read Observational Experiment Table 22.4 in Section 22.2. Here they see that parallel rays diverge after reflection from a convex mirror and seem to come from a single focal point on the other side of the mirror. Students can proceed to ALG activity 22.2.7. Reasoning Skill 22.2 provides explicit instruction for estimating the image distance for different objects at different distances from convex mirrors, and ALG activity 22.2.11 provides them with their first explicit practice at drawing ray diagrams to find the images of objects placed at different distances from a convex mirror. Textbook Conceptual Exercise 22.3 illustrates the nature of images: real or virtual, upright or inverted, and enlarged or reduced in size compared to the object. End-of-chapter questions 4, 5, and 6 and problems 8, 9, and 13 can be used effectively with students in lectures or recitations.

An important issue needs addressing at this point (or you could address it earlier, after concave mirrors, if you like). Students can become so fixated on the principal rays that they have likely forgotten that each point on a light source emits rays in *all* directions. As a result, if you ask students what happens to an image if you cover half of a concave mirror, they will likely think that, since some of the principal rays get cut off, the image will get cut off or chopped in half. You can pose ALG activity 22.2.10 to students in lecture as a clicker question followed by discussion or simply as a discussion question. Make sure you have the actual experiment on hand to demonstrate, once the students have resolved their confusion through discussion. Students should think of this as a testing experiment.

The image location process continues in Section 22.3, only now quantitatively. The object distance s, the image distance s', and the mirror focal length f are introduced in Figure 22.12. A step-by-step derivation of the mirror equation is provided relative to the symbols in that figure. Sign conventions for each of these three quantities are provided following Example 22.5 (it is very important that students understand these sign conventions). Note that there is no accompanying ALG activity for deriving the mirror equation. Next, students need to test the mirror equation. ALG activity 22.3.1 could be used in recitation (since it is a relatively compact table-top experiment) or adapted for a lab. While this activity is relatively simple, we have found that after students have learned some difficult mathematics (here, the mirror equation) it is a very productive experience for them to have to instantiate that equation on real equipment. Students naturally have to confront important questions like "which distances are s and s'?" In figuring out these relatively simple procedural questions, students gain a solid understanding of the equation and the meaning of the symbols involved. Examples 22.4 and 22.5 provide tests of the mirror equation in the textbook. End-of-chapter problems 14–18 can be used effectively with students in lectures or recitations.

Linear magnification is then introduced and related to the image-object distances in Figure 22.15, leading to the linear magnification equation, which is applied in Example 22.7. A tip indicates that the image size and location are independent of the size of the mirrors. A common student mistake is forgetting to invert the $1/s'$ near the end of an example. End-of-chapter problems 19–23 can be used with students in lectures or recitations.

III. Qualitative and Quantitative Analysis of Image Formation by Lenses

You probably have noticed the pattern of development of ideas for mirrors: (1) students conduct observational experiments to find the principal rays, (2) students learn to use ray diagrams to find and describe images that are formed by the mirror, (3) an equation is developed, and (4) students test and apply the equation to real-world situations. The pattern of development for lenses is the same. If students have worked through mirrors already, the development of ideas in this section can go much more quickly, and we recommend developing concave and convex lenses simultaneously. In Observational Experiment Table 22.5 in Section 22.4 (ALG activities 22.1.10 and 22.1.11) students learn about the focal points for convex and concave lenses.

Note that parallel rays that are not parallel to the axis of the lens focus at another point the same distance from the lens as the focal distance, but not on the axis—in the focal plane. With mirrors, there was an activity explicitly addressing this point (ALG activity 22.1.8) but not for lenses; therefore, you need to make sure you mention the similar case for lenses in lecture.

Light passing through a concave lens diverges on the other side but seems to come from a focal point on the same side as the light source. This point from which parallel light seems to diverge is called a virtual focal point. Students should understand that it is a virtual focal point because all light does not actually pass through that point before reaching the lens. ALG activity 22.2.12 is the key activity in which students can practice drawing ray diagrams to locate the position and identify the nature of the image formed by concave and convex lenses. After making their own diagrams, the student can read Reasoning Skill 22.3 to evaluate how they did. This would be a good activity for a lecture. After finishing their diagrams, the student can try to invent a practical application for the lens situation. Students should try a lens Jeopardy problem (Example 22.8 and/or ALG activity 22.4.10)—they are challenging for students and a lot of fun! Conceptual Exercise Example 22.9 involves the effect of covering up part of a lens on the location and size of the image formed by the lens. Make sure to pose this question in lecture for class discussion. End-of-chapter questions 7–10 and 12 and problems 26–30, 75, and 76 can be used with students in lectures or recitations.

In Section 22.5, students can help develop the thin-lens equation and then test it in a lab. ALG activities 22.3.2 and 22.3.3 make an excellent pair of testing experiments that students can conduct in a lab or recitation setting. The equation is derived using the sketch in Figure 22.24. The thin-lens equation is found to survive extreme case evaluation. It is important for students to understand what is meant by a sharp image. The fact that we tend to call a sharp image a focused image in everyday language just adds to the confusion. They must also understand sign conventions used with the thin-lens equation presented in the thin-lens equation definition box. A computer projector example is provided in Example 22.10. Linear magnification is introduced and used in Example 22.11. The tip at the end of the section about not forgetting to invert $1/s'$ to find s' should be emphasized in lectures and recitations. Students can try end-of-chapter problems 32 and 33.

IV. Skills Needed to Solve More Complex Mirror and Lens Problems, Including the Optics of the Eye, Telescopes, and Microscopes

In Example 22.13, the general problem-solving strategy of the book is adapted to problems involving mirrors and lenses. The general strategy is described on the left side of the table and illustrated for a problem on the right side. In Example 22.14, the strategy is applied for shaving and makeup mirrors. Students in lectures or recitations can try ALG activities 22.4.3–22.4.6 and end-of-chapter problems 34, 36, 37, and 38.

Section 22.7, Putting it all together, involves a variety of practical single lens applications, including photography and cameras, the human eye, optics of the eye, near-sighted vision, the power of eyeglass lenses, far-sighted vision, and a final history of lenses. Students in lectures or recitations can work ALG activities 22.4.7, 22.4.9–22.4.15 and end-of-chapter problems 41–46 and 50–56.

V. Angular Magnification, Magnifying Glasses, Telescopes, and Microscopes

In Section 22.8, the deficiency of using only linear magnification is first discussed, followed by the qualitative and quantitative development of the new quantity angular magnification. Angular magnification is applied to a magnifying glass. Students in lectures or recitations can try end-of-chapter problems 58–60.

In Section 22.9, two lens applications are introduced, including the angular magnification of an object viewed through such a two-lens system. Section 22.9 starts with a step-by-step method to locate the image of a two-lens optical system, including the analysis in Figure 22.9. This is very useful for students if you wish to include telescopes and microscopes in your course. The two-lens method is applied to telescopes in Example 22.5 and Figure 22.40 and to microscopes in Example 22.6 and Figure 22.41. Students in lectures or recitations can try end-of-chapter problems 61–64, 67–69, 71–74, and 77 and 78.

23

Wave Optics

In Chapter 21, the first chapter on optics, students learned that observable light phenomena can be explained using ray or particle (bullet-like) models of light and assuming that light behaves similar to a wave. However, we did not resolve the issue and continued to study mirrors and lenses using a particle model of light (represented by light rays). In this chapter, students will learn about experimental evidence that cannot be explained by the particle model and start building the wave model of light.

We focus on interference and diffraction in this chapter and do not touch on the polarization of light, which is covered in the following chapter (Chapter 24, Electromagnetic Waves). Notice there is a slight change of language here—we do not use the term diffraction grating but instead call the gratings interference gratings, the reason being that when we study diffraction, the slits are not considered infinitely narrow. We discuss the interference of light produced by different parts of the same slit. Because this model is not applicable to the grating (where light that passes through different slits interferes on the screen), we do not call it a diffraction grating.

This chapter is broken into five parts:

I. *Young's double-slit experiment and multiple-slit gratings*
II. *The relation between index of refraction, light speed, and wave coherence*
III. *Thin-film interference*
IV. *Diffraction of light and resolving power*
V. *Skills for analyzing processes involving light waves*

For each part, we describe activities can be used in lecture and recitations to help students acquire these ideas and the motivation for using these activities.

Chapter subject matter	Related textbook section	ALG activities	End-of-chapter questions and problems	Videos
Young's double-slit experiment and multiple-slit gratings	23.1, 23.3	23.1.1–23.1.3, 23.2.1, 23.2.2, 23.3.1–23.3.4, 23.3.6–23.3.8, 23.4.5	Questions 1, 2, 4, 6 Problems 2–5, 7, 11–14, 16, 17, 57, 59	23.1, 23.2
The relation between index of refraction, light speed, and wave coherence	23.2		Questions 2, 5, 8 Problem 8	
Thin-film interference	23.4		Problems 21–23	23.3
Diffraction of light and resolving power	23.5, 23.6	23.2.3, 23.3.9, 23.3.10	Question 7 Problems 28–31, 33, 37, 38, 40, 60, 63–67	23.5
Skills for analyzing processes invol-ving light waves	23.7	23.4.5, 23.4.6, 23.4.8	Problems 35, 42–44, 46–55	

I. Young's Double-Slit Experiment and Multiple-Slit Gratings

The investigation starts with students reviewing two models of light that they have constructed in Chapter 21: the bullet model and the wave model. Active Learning Guide (ALG) activity 23.1.1 invites them to explain three familiar phenomena: shadows, reflection, and refraction. If students start this chapter in a lab, they can work in groups performing the suggested experiments and then explain them in the provided table. If you start in lecture, you can show the experiments as demos and invite students to explain the results. They should use the bullet model, which can easily explain shadows and reflection (impulse momentum ideas), and the wave model (Huygens's principle) to explain refraction. They might have difficulties explaining refraction using the bullet model—remind them of the explanation provided in Chapter 21. This is just a brief review of Chapters 20 and 21. But overall, students should feel that the particle model of light can explain all of the light phenomena they have observed so far.

A new testing experiment (ALG activity 23.1.2 and textbook Testing Experiment Table 23.2) involves asking students to predict what happens when light from a light source passes through two closely positioned, narrow slits. Students make a prediction based on the particle model of light and observe that the pattern on a screen does not match the prediction (Testing Experiment Table 23.1). However, the wave model combined with Huygens's principle matches the outcome of the experiment (Example 23.1 and ALG activities 23.1.3, 23.2.1, and 23.2.2).

Following this qualitative introduction to double-slit interference, students can analyze double-slit interference quantitatively by using ALG activities 23.3.1 and 23.3.2 (these are best if students are in a lab and actually perform the testing experiment). You can lead them through the derivation in a class discussion using textbook Figure 23.2 for the 0th and 1st order maxima equal from the two slits to the screen and Figure 23.3 for the general expression for the *m*th order bright band. The relationship is then tested and summarized for *bright* bands. Notice the tip following the summary box on page 857. It adapts the interference expression for the dark bands of the interference pattern on the screen.

Note that both the ALG and the textbook lead students first through the qualitative analysis of the interference process, and only after students understand what happens conceptually is the quantitative expression introduced/derived. The textbook also addresses a possible question that students might have at this point: if light is analogous to a wave, then what is oscillating in that wave? We do not provide an answer to this question yet, but only start the discussion; the answer will appear in Chapter 24 on electromagnetic waves. Help students work through Quantitative Exercise 23.1 to determine the wavelength of green light. End-of-chapter questions 1 and 2 and problems 2–5, 7, and 57 can be used with students in lectures or recitations.

ALG activities 23.3.3 and 23.3.4 and textbook Section 23.3 are dedicated to the interference grating, a system of multiple, narrow slits. Remind students that the distance d between adjacent slits is $d = 1/_{(\text{\# of slits/cm})}$. A qualitative analysis in the textbook of the interference process that occurs when there are more than two slits (in which we slowly add slits one by one and observe that the brightness of the bands increases and the width of the bright bands decreases) proceeds to the derivation of the quantitative expression in Quantitative Exercise 23.3. Now students can apply grating-related concepts to the interference of white light, a reflection grating from a CD and a DVD, and a spectrometer used to analyze spectral composition of light from a particular light source (see Example 23.4 for analysis of an H-atom spectrum).

ALG activity 23.3.6 addresses a difficulty that students sometimes have understanding—that it is the total number of slits that determines how the interference pattern looks. Students are invited to test this idea in a lab. Other ALG activities conceived as lab experiments are 23.3.7, 23.3.8, and 23.4.5. You can use end-of-chapter questions 4 and 6 and problems 11–14, 16–17, and 59 in lectures or recitations.

II. The Relation Between Index of Refraction, Light Speed, and Wave Coherence

Section 23.2 concerns important ideas that are necessary for light interference—monochromatic and coherent light sources. The section starts with a derivation of a relationship between the index of refraction n of a medium and the speed of light v in that medium $n = c/v$. A tip early in the section reminds students that the frequency of a light wave depends on the wave source and does not change as the wave passes from one medium to another. Thus, if the speed v changes from one medium to another, the wavelength λ also changes but not the frequency. A discussion of chromatic aberration of camera lenses is provided. Finally, the section focuses on monochromatic and coherent sources of light. We provide motivation for this discussion by asking a question: "Why can we not use two light bulbs to observe an interference pattern on a screen?" The discussion is extremely important because an understanding of coherent waves is necessary for the comprehension of the thin-film interference that follows. Thus we suggest that you run a discussion in class concerning these issues and then encourage the students to read the textbook for additional exposure. Use end-of-chapter questions 2, 5, and 8 and problem 8 in lectures or recitations.

III. Thin-Film Interference

Section 23.4 is dedicated to thin-film interference. Let students observe the colors of a soap bubble before you proceed to the explanation. If you have a large class and are doing this in a lecture, we suggest that you set up a few containers with soap solution and wire frames with a side of 7–9 cm so students can see the film clearly. A video of the bubble is good, but nothing can substitute for a careful observation of the phenomenon. Everyone has seen this before, but they have not concentrated on the details. After students have had an opportunity to marvel at the colors of the bubble and observe the black color of the film on the top of the frame right before the film breaks, you can proceed to helping students develop the explanation of the phenomenon in the simpler case of monochromatic light.

Several factors are important for this explanation: (a) light reflected from the front surface of the film and the back inside surface of the film interfere with each other; (b) a reflection leads to a phase change if the medium off which light reflects is optically denser than the first medium; (c) additional phase difference occurs due to the path length difference of the light traveling through the film and back out. This latter path length phase difference depends on the wavelength of the light while in the film (and on the index of refraction of that film). All these factors contribute to the resulting interference if the film is thin enough for all of the waves to remain coherent. We test the explanation in Testing Experiment Table 23.3 to predict what students would see just before a soap bubble pops (when its thickness becomes very small due to sagging and evaporation). We apply these same two phase-change ideas for other examples in this section, such as thin-film interference on a glass surface. Table 23.4 provides a summary of thin-film interference examples for monochromatic light. The section ends with more-detailed discussions of four interesting applications: (1) the continuous change in a soap bubble color as its thickness changes due to evaporation; (2) the complimentary (as opposed to rainbow) colors of the soap films irradiated by white light; (3) use of thin films on the lenses of optical instruments to reduce reflection; and (4) the color of light reflected from some birds and from butterflies. End-of-chapter problems 21–23 can be used with students in lectures or recitations. There is no parallel ALG material.

IV. Diffraction of Light and Resolving Power

The next big theme is diffraction. If your students are starting diffraction in a lab, they can do ALG activity 23.2.3, or you can use it as a demonstration, keeping the spirit of the observational experiment, and then proceed to the quantitative explanation using ALG activity 23.3.9. Students can work in groups of twos, answering the questions in this activity, followed by a whole-class discussion of the derivation, which can be followed by the testing experiment described in ALG activity 23.3.10. This logical progression is repeated in Section 23.5, which starts with Observational Experiment Table 23.5 describing what happens when light passes through single slits of different thicknesses. Students learn that the *diffraction pattern* of the transmitted light broadens as the slit thickness decreases. This is followed by a quantitative analysis of single-slit diffraction (see Figure 23.24).

It is important to remind students that the equation describing single-slit diffraction applies to the angular deflection of the *dark bands* and not the bright bands, which are used for the bright bands in double-slit interference and grating interference.

Notice the discussion about the Poisson spot experiment, which provides a very interesting example of the process of science. Poisson did not support the wave explanation for diffraction. He considered it false because the prediction that followed from the wave model for the situation when light passes around a small ball seemed ridiculous, and he expected that it would not be observed: there should be a bright spot at the center of the shadow of a small ball irradiated by light. To his surprise, the bright spot was there! It provided support for the wave theory for diffraction. Section 23.5 ends with everyday examples of diffraction, including why we hear sound in all parts of a room with a tiny opening in the door but see only a bright band of light coming from outside into the room. Students in lectures or recitations can try end-of-chapter problems 28–31 and 60.

Section 23.6 concerns the resolving ability of circular lenses, including light entering the pupil of the eye. Why, for example, is it better to have a large telescope lens than a small one in order to detect small details on a distant object? Students in lectures or recitations can try end-of-chapter question 7 and problems 33, 37, 38, 40, 63–67, and 69.

V. Skills for Analyzing Processes Involving Light Interference

Example 23.8 in Section 23.7 adapts the general problem-solving strategy of the textbook to problems involving light interference. The general strategy is described on the left side of the table solution for Example 23.8 and illustrated for a problem on the right side. In Example 23.9, the strategy is applied to using diffraction to determine the size of a red blood cell. Students in lectures or recitations can try end-of-chapter problems 35, 42–44, and 46–55. ALG activities in Section 23.4 provide a nice variety of word and experimental problems for the interference/diffraction concepts. Specifically, ALG activities 23.4.5 and 23.4.6 can be used as experiments in the labs, and activity 23.4.8 is a good lead into the observational experiments for special relativity (in Chapter 25).

24 Electromagnetic Waves

In Chapter 23, students learned the wave model of light and used it to explain what happens when light passes through narrow openings or reflects off thin films. Although the wave model of light is successful in explaining and predicting a great variety of light-related phenomena, it does not contain the mechanism of the wave motion. Specifically, it does not explain what physical quantities change inside the light wave. In this chapter, students learn the electromagnetic nature of the light waves through the analysis of simple experiments and subsequent testing of the newly constructed explanations. The chapter is broken into five parts:

I. *Polarization of waves*
II. *The discovery of electromagnetic waves*
III. *Some important applications of electromagnetic waves*
IV. *The electromagnetic spectrum and a quantitative description of waves*
V. *Polarization and light reflection*

For each part, we describe the sequence of activities that can be used in lecture and recitations to help students develop these ideas. We also provide brief discussions of motivations for using these activities.

Chapter subject matter	Related textbook section	ALG activities	End-of-chapter questions and problems	Videos
Polarization of waves	24.1	24.1.1, 24.1.2, 24.3.1	Questions 1, 2 Problems 1–3	24.1, 24.2

Discovery of electromagnetic waves	24.2	24.2.2, 24.3.2	Questions 8, 9	
Some important applications of electromagnetic waves	24.3	24.1.1–24.1.4	Problems 14, 16, 18	
The electromagnetic spectrum and a quantitative description of waves	24.4, 24.5	23.3.3–23.3.5, 24.4.5, 24.4.6	Question 10 Problems 19, 25–27, 30, 34–37, 49	24.4
Polarization and light reflection	24.6	24.3.6, 24.3.7	Question 12 Problems 43, 44	

I. Polarization of Waves

Although students learned about several types of experiments that can be explained with the wave model, Chapter 23 did not touch on the polarization of waves. Polarization is the subject of this section.

It is important that students get a firm conceptual grounding of polarization in the context of mechanical waves. Thus, this section invites students to explore polarization in the context of transverse and longitudinal waves on a Slinky. In Observational Experiment Table 24.1, students observe that transverse mechanical waves can be polarized but longitudinal mechanical waves cannot. This is an excellent activity to do as a lecture demonstration, or have students perform experiments on their own; the matching activity in the Active Learning Guide (ALG) is 24.1.1. Students devise an explanation for these observations. They then observe that light can be polarized in a similar way to mechanical waves, leading to the hypothesis that light is a transverse wave. This is followed by a quantitative analysis of the effect of polarizers on light (ALG Activity 24.1.2 or textbook Observational Experiment Table 24.2).

The intensity of light passing through two polarizers decreases in proportion to the square of the cosine of the angle between the polarizers (ALG activity 24.3.1). Students have concluded that it is a transverse wave; however, what is vibrating in a transverse manner in the light wave is still a mystery. The section ends with two hypotheses concerning the mechanism for the transverse light wave: light travels in a transparent massless elastic medium called the ether, or light is a new type of wave that doesn't require a medium to travel in. Use end-of-chapter questions 1 and 2 and problems 1–3 in lectures or recitations.

II. The Discovery of Electromagnetic Waves

Because the mechanism that explains how a wave propagating in a vacuum can be transverse involves electric and magnetic fields, students need to review those and the relationships among them. Section 24.2 starts with a qualitative summary of Maxwell's equations. We then discuss one of the consequences of the equations, that a changing electric field can produce a changing magnetic field, which in turn can produce a changing electric field, and on and on in a sort of feedback loop. Figure 24.6 illustrates this process. Thus one can conceptualize a light wave as a wave of changing electric and magnetic fields whose $\vec{E}$ and $\vec{B}$ vectors are perpendicular to the direction of wave propagation; hence the mechanism explaining how a transverse wave can propagate in a vacuum. The equations even predict the speed c of the waves in a vacuum (ALG activity 24.3.2).

The development of an understanding of electromagnetic waves is an excellent example of how physics develops as encapsulated in the Investigative Science Learning Environment cycle. This idea that electromagnetic waves could propagate without a medium was first tested in experiments by Hertz (Testing Experiment Table 24.3). If you are running a process-focused physics course, you can have students read the textbook section about Hertz's experiments and how they tested various aspects of Maxwell's hypothesis about electromagnetic waves. This development quickly leads to applications such as transmitting information via radio waves. The end of Section 24.2 is dedicated to the emission of electromagnetic waves by antennas and to a conceptual explanation of the phase difference between the $\vec{E}$ and the $\vec{B}$ field vectors in a wave (in phase) compared to the phase difference in the antenna ($\pi/2$) (see Figure 24.8).

It is a real accomplishment if your students can build a conceptual understanding of how a simple half-wave dipole antenna can produce an electromagnetic wave when driven by an oscillating emf. We recommend that students start this section with ALG activity 24.2.2. This activity helps them build up a detailed step-by-step picture as the antenna passes through one complete charging cycle. Once they have this understanding, they can work through the end of textbook Section 24.2 with you in lecture or on their own. Here they learn that these antenna fields are called near fields (with the phase shift), which later, after leaving the antenna, progress by self-propagation to produce so-called far field waves (in phase). Students can then work on the end-of-chapter questions 8 and 9.

III. Some Important Applications of Electromagnetic Waves

Three important applications of electromagnetic waves are the subject of Section 24.3: (1) the operation of radar for keeping track of air vehicles, specifically, the longest and shortest distances to objects that can be detected with a particular radar; (2) the way in which the global positioning system works, including triangulation; and

(3) the interesting history and the details of the operation of microwave cooking. You can use end-of-chapter problems 14, 16, and 18 and ALG activities 24.4.1–24.4.4 with students in lectures or recitations. Note that in the first application (radar), we do not get into the details of pulsed Doppler radar but stick with the most elementary radar, in which location and speed of a moving object are determined by the time interval between received and transmitted pulses.

IV. The Electromagnetic Spectrum and a Quantitative Description of Waves

Section 24.4 is dedicated to the physical quantities of frequency and wavelength describing electromagnetic waves and the electromagnetic spectrum (see Table 24.4). It is important that the word spectrum stand in this case for the range of electromagnetic waves in terms of their frequency, not the energy distribution versus frequency, which is another meaning of this word. Section 24.5 follows with the mathematical description of electromagnetic waves and their energy. We use unit analysis to show that $E_{max} = cB_{max}$ and use this relation as well as the in-phase arguments developed earlier to create mathematical functions describing the electromagnetic waves (matching ALG activities are 23.3.3–23.3.5). Notice textbook Figure 24.15 shows how to use the right-hand rule to relate the $\vec{E}$ and the $\vec{B}$ field vectors and the travel direction of the wave. The section also shows how to develop the expressions for the energy and the intensity of the waves. We apply the knowledge of intensity to the solar constant in Example 24.3. Students in lectures or recitations can try ALG activities 24.4.5 and 6 and end-of-chapter question 10 and problems 19, 25–27, 30, 34–37, and 49.

V. Polarization and Light Reflection

Students learned at the beginning of the chapter that light could be polarized. Section 24.6 returns to the subject at a new level. First, students learn the mechanism behind the production of unpolarized light and then study a simplified model of a polarizer and its interaction with light. The section gets into the mechanism of light polarization, whereas the first section merely discussed the existence of the phenomenon. The next step is learning about the polarization by reflection and the Brewster angle. Students can perform the experiments described in the textbook Observational Experiment Table 24.5 in the labs, or you can perform demo experiments in a lecture setting. Ask the students to analyze the observed phenomena following the guidance provided in the table or ALG activity 24.3.6, and then have them work through ALG activity 24.3.7 to lead them to the final result of the Brewster angle (Equation 24.6). Example 24.4 involves reducing glare of reflected light. The polarization by scattering includes an analysis of why the sky is blue and sunsets are red (Figures 24.24 and 24.25). The polarization of light from LCDs is analyzed in Figure 24.27. The role of polarization in 3D movies is the subject of the last part of the section (Figure 24.28). Students in lectures or recitations can try end-of-chapter question 12 and problems 43 and 44.

25

Special Relativity

In the previous four chapters, students learned the nature of light and its applications. We now start five chapters concerning contemporary physics involving quantum concepts and wave/particle duality of light and matter. This chapter, on relativity, is broken into seven parts. For each part, we describe the sequences of activities that can be used in class to help students acquire these ideas and brief discussions of the motivation for using these activities.

I. *Ether, postulates of special relativity, and simultaneity*
II. *Time dilation and length contraction*
III. *Velocity transformations*
IV. *Relativistic momentum and energy*
V. *The Doppler effect for electromagnetic waves*
VI. *General relativity*
VII. *Global Positioning Systems*

Chapter subject matter	Related textbook section	ALG activities	End-of-chapter questions and problems
Ether, postulates of special relativity, and simultaneity	25.1–25.3	25.1.1, 25.1.2, 25.2.2, 25.2.3	Questions 1, 2, 7, 8
Time dilation and length contraction	25.4, 25.5	25.2.1, 25.3.1, 25.4.1, 25.4.2	Questions 4, 5, 6, 9 Problems 8–15, 18–21, 61–63
Velocity transformations	25.6	25.3.2, 25.4.6	Problems 25–27

Relativistic momentum and energy	25.7, 25.8	25.3.3, 25.3.4, 25.4.3, 25.4.4	Question 12 Problems 30, 33–46, 48, 49, 51, 53, 65, 66
The Doppler effect for electromagnetic waves	25.9	25.4.9	Problems 55, 58, 59
General relativity	25.10		Question 10
Global positioning systems	25.11		Question 11

It is important to note that this is the first chapter where students cannot perform actual experiments. Most of the experiments are thought experiments or historical experiments. Therefore, careful planning of the activities and engaging students in discussions is very important here. You might use the textbook sections and Active Learning Guide (ALG) activities as a basis for class discussions and then let students read the textbook and go through worked examples on their own. Conceptually, what unifies all the sections in this chapter is the use of the "need to know" approach. Although many of the equations (especially in the second part of the chapter) cannot be derived in this course, we can definitely provide a motivation for the students for why new, relativistic expressions for familiar quantities are needed, thus creating "the need to know" these new expressions.

I. Ether, Postulates of Special Relativity, and Simultaneity

Although students have learned about electromagnetic waves that do not need any medium to travel through, historically physicists thought that light waves needed a medium to travel (polarization of light created the need for a medium where sheer deformations could occur). Thus, they invented ether as the medium through which light propagates. How could one test the existence of ether? To understand the essence of the Michelson-Morley experiment that is an example of a testing experiment for the model of ether, students can use the boat analogy (textbook Section 25.1). Notice that we have not done traditional up-down-across stream boat problems in the kinematics chapter intentionally because we planned to return to the concept of relative motion here.

Specifically, there is a boat race in a stream. One boat traveled up a stream and back down. The second boat traveled the same distance relative to the shore but across the stream and back. Using classical analysis, we find that the upstream-downstream trip should take longer than the across and back stream trip. This type of thinking led to a test for the ether performed by Michelson and Morley (see Testing Experiment Table 25.1). No ether was found. Therefore, the concept of ether can be discarded. We suggest that you lead students through this logical progression and assign end-of-chapter questions 1 and 2.

Independently of the Michelson-Morley experiment, Einstein (based on thought experiments) proposed two postulates that formed the basis for special relativity (see Section 25.2). The most controversial postulate was that light travels at the same speed in all inertial reference frames independent of the velocities of these reference frames relative to each other. Students can do ALG activities 25.1.1 and 25.1.2 to build a foundation for this postulate and read Section 25.2. Near the end of the section there is a discussion of a testing experiment for the postulate that involved the speed of gamma rays produced by pion decay. The gamma rays moved at the speed of light in a lab reference frame in which the pions were moving at slightly less than the speed of light. Students can proceed to questions 7 and 8 and ALG activity 25.2.2. Section 25.3 involves a discussion of events and the possibility that events occurred simultaneously in one inertial reference frame but not in another (see ALG activity 25.2.3).

II. Time Dilation and Length Contraction

Section 25.4 involves a derivation of time dilation and the introduction of the proper time between two events, which occur at the same place in a particular inertial reference frame. It is important for students to understand which reference frame is considered the proper reference frame. The idea of time dilation is tested in Testing Experiment Table 25.2 by considering muon production in the atmosphere—muons that would be unable to travel to Earth's surface if it were not for time dilation (use ALG activity 25.3.1 for students to derive the prediction). Quantitative Exercise 25.1 considers the measurement of a person's heart rate by an observer on a spaceship in which the person is traveling very fast relative to an observer on Earth. Use ALG activities 25.2.1 and 25.4.1 and textbook end-of-chapter questions 4, 5, and 9 and problems 8–15 and 61–63 with students in lectures or recitations.

Section 25.5 involves a derivation of an expression for length contraction. After you lead students through the derivation, they can apply the contraction idea to explain the interaction of two current-carrying wires (ALG activity 25.2.4). Quantitative Exercise 25.2 helps students get a "feeling" for the length contraction of an arrow moving at high speed and at normal speed. Notice that we use the binomial expansion for the latter calculation. Example 25.3 is a story of an event observed in a universe with a low speed of light. Use end-of-chapter question 6 and problems 18–21 with students in lectures or recitations.

III. Velocity Transformations

Section 25.6 starts with the derivation of the Galilean velocity transformation. The outcome of the derivation is the expression that makes sense for the students intuitively. To foster students' "need to know" the relativistic velocity transformation, we show that the classical way of adding velocities does not work for high speeds. We do not derive the expression for a relativistic velocity transformation; we provide it without the derivation and ask the students to evaluate its application to the known limiting cases (ALG activity 25.3.2). You might follow the same strategy in class. ALG activity 25.4.6 and end-of-chapter problems 25–27 can be used with students in lectures or recitations.

IV. Relativistic Momentum and Energy

Students learn that momentum, when calculated using the classical definition, stops being a conserved quantity (here students need to take this conclusion on faith, as we do not provide data to support this idea), and this finding motivates the relativistic expression for momentum. We derive a relativistic expression for momentum by replacing the Δt in the classical expression by the proper time from the time dilation equation. Students can use this new relativistic expression for the momentum expression when analyzing a cosmic ray hitting a nitrogen nucleus in Example 25.4. Students can work on ALG activities 25.3.3 and 25.3.4 and textbook end-of-chapter question 12 and problems 30 and 33.

To motivate the new expression, students can conduct classical energy analysis of the electron that passes through a potential difference of 300,000 V. They will find that the electron would be traveling at a speed greater than the speed of light (Section 25.8). This finding means that energy expressions must also be revised for relativistic situations. We provide new relativistic expressions for particle rest energy, total energy, and kinetic energy without proof, and students can apply the new expressions in Quantitative Exercise 25.6 that determines the mass energy equivalent needed to warm a home in winter and cool it in summer for one year—about 2×10^{-7} kg! Example 25.7 analyzes an electron particle accelerator. Students in lectures or recitations can try end-of-chapter problems 34–46, 48, 49, 51, 53, 65, and 66 and ALG activities 25.4.3 and 25.4.4.

V. The Doppler Effect for Electromagnetic Waves

Section 25.9 starts with building the "need" for a new expression for the Doppler effect for electromagnetic waves compared to sound waves as the result of the postulates of special relativity. We treat the Doppler effect traditionally by providing the expression for electromagnetic radiation for high and low speeds. There is a brief discussion of the red shift in astronomy. Example 25.8 discusses the use of Doppler radar for determining an automobile speed and the speed of baseballs and tennis balls. There is a discussion of evidence for the expanding universe as observed and measured by Edwin Hubble and Milton Humason, leading to an estimate of the age of the universe. Students in lectures or recitations can try end-of-chapter problems 55, 58, and 59 and ALG activity 25.4.9.

VI. General Relativity

Section 25.10 introduces students to the principle of equivalence, along with the idea of space curvature. We describe testing this idea in the historical experiments of starlight bent as it passes the Sun and also by the speed of precession of Mercury about the Sun. We touch upon gravitational time dilation and red shift along with gravitational waves and black holes. Students in lectures or recitations can try end-of-chapter question 10.

VII. Global Positioning Systems

Section 25.11 discusses the way in which global positioning systems (GPS) work, along with the effect of special relativity and general relativity on GPS location. Students in lectures or recitations can try end-of-chapter question 11.

26

Quantum Optics

In this chapter, we build the photon model light. Students have been developing their understanding of light for quite some time now. In Chapter 21 they started with a simple ray model and then learned that the ray-like behavior can be explained by assuming that light behaved like a stream of low-mass fast bullets (particle model) or with the wave model. In Chapter 23 they encountered experimental evidence that could not be explained with the particle model at all and developed more confidence in the wave model of light. Later (Chapter 24) they learned what was "waving" in the light wave and revised their model of light again to arrive at the electromagnetic wave model.

In this chapter, they revisit the behavior of light one more time and revise the model of light. This complex process reflects the complex nature of light: it cannot be adequately compared to any macroscopic object, and that is why the final model of light that the students will learn in this book—the photon model—is full of apparent contradictions. Neither the particle nor the wave model on its own can explain and predict light behavior completely. Only a model that combines those two contradictory ideas into one entity—a photon, which is not a particle and is not a wave but possesses the properties of both—can satisfy the demands of light as a real phenomenon. Because the photon model of light introduces students to something with which they have no direct experience, they often oversimplify it, thinking that it is just a particle model with a different name. The goal of this chapter is to help students avoid this confusion. We've broken the discussion of this chapter into three parts:

I. *Quantum (photon) model of EM radiation*
II. *X-rays and X-ray interference*
III. *Photocells and solar cells*

For each part, we provide examples of activities that can be used in the classroom and brief discussions of anticipated student difficulties with the subject matter. Because there are few simple experiments that students can perform in the chapter, the Active Learning Guide (ALG) activities are limited, and the bulk of the problem solving should be based on the material in the end-of-chapter problems.

Chapter subject matter	Related textbook section	ALG activities	End-of-chapter questions and problems
Quantum (photon) model of EM radiation	26.1–26.4	26.1.1–26.1.5, 26.3.1, 26.3.3–26.3.5, 26.4.1–26.4.6	Questions 2, 3 Problems 1, 2, 3, 6, 7, 14–17, 20, 24, 27, 28, 30, 52, 54, 56
X-rays and X-ray interference	26.5, 26.6	26.3.7	Problems 40, 42
Photocells and solar cells	26.7		Problems 45, 48, 50

I. Quantum (Photon) Model of EM Radiation

The goal of Section 26.1 is to introduce students to the quantum hypothesis that was born as an attempt to explain how objects radiate light (black body radiation). Students learn about black bodies and observational evidence related to their emission of light, including Stefan's law and Wien's law. These are useful in general for applications concerning radiation from the Sun (see Quantitative Exercise 26.1), the stars, and in general for ideas related to body temperature and global temperature control. However, the main emphasis of this section is the failed efforts in the late 1800s to explain the intensity-versus-frequency spectrum of black body radiation using the wave model of light and Planck's quantum hypothesis, which did provide an explanation for this radiation and initiated the idea of quanta of light. The mathematical details of Planck's light quanta idea for black body radiation are beyond the grasp of the students in this course, but the concept of light emission as quanta is very important for the upcoming investigation of the photoelectric effect. Students can try end-of-chapter questions 2 and 3 or problems 1, 2, 3, 6, 7, or 52 in recitations or lectures.

Textbook Section 26.2 is dedicated to the photoelectric effect but starts with a short review of the structure of metals. Students are already familiar with the classical models of metal structure from Chapter 16. What is important here is the emphasis on the electric potential energy of the electron-ion lattice system, which is negative (if we consider the system to have zero energy when the electron is not interacting with the lattice). The minimum positive energy needed to remove a negative electron from the metal is called the work function (ϕ, Greek phi). Thus, the energy of interaction of the electron with the lattice is $-\phi$. The investigation of the photoelectric effect starts with experiments in which ultraviolet light discharges a charged electroscope. You can use ALG activity 26.1.1 in lecture; the experiment can be performed as a class demonstration and the students can answer the question posed in the activity. They can also read Observational Experiment Table 26.2, which summarizes experiments in which ultraviolet light discharges a negatively charged electroscope (whereas visible light does not). Neither ultraviolet nor visible light discharge a positively charged electroscope.

After students perform the activities described in Table 26.2, it is useful to discuss possible mechanisms that can explain why light would have an effect on a charged electroscope and why it only discharges a negatively charged electroscope and not a positively charged one (see ALG activity 26.1.2 and two proposed explanations in the textbook after Table 26.2). After students devise a qualitative mechanism for the discharge of the electroscope by electromagnetic waves, they can proceed to more detailed investigations of the phenomenon. ALG activity 26.1.3 and textbook Observational Experiment Table 26.3 describe historical experiments performed by Lenard, including important patterns he observed (note that in the textbook we emphasize that for some metals even visible light can produce the same effect as the ultraviolet).

Engage students in the discussion to explain the patterns (ALG activities 26.1.3–26.1.5). ALG activity 26.1.3 is an activity that may be worth spending a little extra time on. It requires students to coordinate their understanding of circuits and electrical potential to comprehend what is happening in the experiment. This is very challenging for them and takes time. However, this activity can be used to reintroduce earlier ideas and reinforce the usefulness of their understanding of electrical phenomena for understanding real-world experiments.

Make sure that you use the energy bar charts to help them represent the process (the textbook guides students with this revised representation). Students will be able to explain some of them using the electromagnetic wave model of light (with your help and guidance) but not the cutoff frequency, stopping potential, and the immediate nature of the phenomenon. The key point is that students need to realize that there are aspects of this experiment that the wave model of light cannot explain. Thus, a new model of light is needed to explain all of the observations. Remind students about Planck's hypothesis explaining the emission of light using the quantum idea and ask if a similar idea could be used to explain the patterns for the electric effect. In rare cases, students construct the "photon" model during such discussions. At home, students can try question 4.

Section 26.3 introduces students to Einstein's photon model and shows how it is consistent with all of the experiments in Table 26.3. They can work on ALG activities 26.3.1–26.3.1 to see how the photon model explains all of the observed patterns qualitatively. Note that we write the photoelectric effect equation $-\phi + hf = K_e$ so that we can represent the process using a bar chart. Here the negative value of the work function represents the initial potential energy of the electron-lattice system, hf is the energy added to the system, and K_e is the final energy of the electron. Table 26.4 describes a simple testing experiment for the photon explanation of the photoelectric effect. We provide the summary of how Einstein's theory addressed the observations of the photoelectric experiment near the end of the section, along with a definition of a photon. Finally, make sure that students work through Example 26.6, which shows how to combine the energy bar chart analysis with the mathematics to analyze photoelectric effect problems. Students can work on ALG activities 26.4.1–26.4.6 and end-of-chapter problems 14–17 in recitations, lectures, or homework.

The goal of Section 26.4 is to deepen students' understanding of the complex nature of light. Table 26.3 in Section 26.4 describes the evolution of the light models that followed the increased experimental sophistication of those physicists who worked with light. It is important that students slow down here and really think of the properties of photons that allow them to explain all of the existing experimental evidence. A photon is not just a light particle; it is an object that has simultaneously particle-like and wave-like properties. An exciting experiment with low-intensity light provides more evidence for these unique properties of photons that do not have any analogues in our macroscopic world.

We suggest that you first let students work though ALG activity 26.3.3, which represents Vavilov-Brumberg's experiment, and read Testing Experiment Table 26.6. ALG activity 26.3.4 is very useful here to help students consolidate the understanding of the photon's peculiar properties and develop argumentation skills. A relatively simple derivation of photon momentum occurs at the end of the textbook section (parallel to ALG activity 26.3.5). Students can work on end-of-chapter problems 20, 24, 27, 28, 30, 54, and 56 in recitations, lectures, or homework.

II. X-rays and X-ray Interference

The goal of textbook Section 26.5 is to introduce students to X-rays as photons of energy higher than that of visible light. We use the historical path here, moving from cathode ray tubes and the discovery of the electrons to the discovery of X-rays by Roentgen, who was working with cathode ray tubes. There are two important points here. First, careful analysis of cathode rays allows the students to review mechanics and magnetic fields material. Second, Roentgen's accidental discovery of X-rays provides a particularly interesting example of the practice of science and the importance of careful observation and testing. The section describes the investigations that showed that properties of X-rays had all the properties of EM radiation, only with much shorter wavelength than other forms of this radiation known at the time. However, the fact that X-rays ionize gases provides the need for the photon model. Students can work on end-of-chapter problems 34, 37, and 38 in recitations or lectures.

ALG activities 26.3.7–26.3.7 and Section 26.6 continue investigations of X-rays, describing experiments that provided additional evidence that X-rays are photons of high energy that have momentum. Notice our treatment of Compton's experiments as testing experiments for the photon nature of X-rays, both in the ALG and the textbook. The dual nature of the photons possessing both wave and particle properties allows us to predict the changes in the wavelengths of light colliding with electrons using momentum conservation and Planck's equation and to explain interference patterns they produce when passing through periodic crystals. X-rays provide a good connection to medicine. Note Quantitative Exercises 26.10 and 26.11 that provide estimates of the number of X-ray photons absorbed during a chest X-ray and the number absorbed from background radiation from our environment. Problems that students in lectures and recitations can work to help develop qualitative and quantitative understanding include 40 and 42.

III. Photocells and Solar Cells

We use photocells and solar cells as examples of many interesting applications of photoelectric effect in Section 26.7. We provide a qualitative introduction to solar cells, including the review of the nature of semiconductors, the new material for the p-type and n-type doping semiconductors, p-n junctions, and the role of the p-n junction in the creation of a battery in the presence of light. You can assign end-of-chapter problems 45, 48, and 50 in lectures.

27

Atomic Physics

In Chapter 26, students learned about the dual wave-particle nature of light. In this chapter, these ideas are used to help build atomic models to account for observations in early atomic physics and to develop the concept of the dual wave-particle nature of elementary particles. We continue to use the representations that students are already familiar with, such as force diagrams and energy bar charts, but in addition we introduce a new representation—the energy states diagram. We also are careful about language usage. Because an electron by itself can only have kinetic energy, we do not talk about the electron energy levels in the atom but instead talk about the energy states of the atom. This wording assumes that the kinetic energy of the nucleus is zero.

This chapter is broken into five parts:

I. *Early atomic models*
II. *Bohr's model of the atom*
III. *Spectral analysis and lasers*
IV. *Quantum nature of atoms, the exclusion principle, and many-electron atoms*
V. *The uncertainty principle*

For each part, we provide examples of activities that can be used in the classroom and brief discussions of anticipated student difficulties with the subject matter.

Chapter subject matter	Related textbook section	ALG activities	End-of-chapter questions and problems
Early atomic models	27.1	27.1.1–27.1.6	Problems 2–4
Bohr's model of the atom	27.2	27.1.7, 27.2.3, 27.3.1–27.3.9	Questions 3, 4 Problems 8, 9, 20, 64, 66

Spectral analysis and lasers	27.3, 27.4	27.3.8, 27.3.9, 27.4.1–27.4.10, 27.4.12	Problems 14, 22, 27, 28
Quantum nature of atoms, the exclusion principle, and many-electron atoms	27.5–27.7	27.1.8, 27.1.9, 27.2.4, 27.3.10, 27.3.11	Question 12 Problems 39–41, 43, 44, 46, 47, 49
The uncertainty principle	27.8		Problems 55–58

I. Early Atomic Models

A discussion of experiments leading to the "plum pudding" model and the Rutherford orbital models of the atom (Section 27.1) provides an excellent chance to help students base model building on experimental observations. Active Learning Guide (ALG) activities 27.1.1 and 27.1.2 provide such observational experiments for the students and start their reasoning process concerning the structure of the particles that produce line spectra (activity 27.1.1 is easy to reproduce in a lab or project on the screen in a lecture setting) or allow electrons to pass through undeflected (activity 27.1.2).

Because students are familiar with the plum pudding model of the atoms, you can focus their attention on how this model can account for the observational evidence. For example, you could ask students to think briefly about what type of scattering you might expect from electrons shot at a thin sheet of plum pudding atoms. Then ask them to reconcile their thinking with that of neighboring students. Proceed to ALG activity 27.1.3, which describes the Geiger and Marsden experiments of alpha particle scattering. ALG activity 27.1.4 helps students understand the nature of the experiment and the reasoning process through which Rutherford might have arrived at the nuclear model of the atom. ALG activities 27.1.5 and 27.1.6 help them understand the model in depth. Section 27.1 ends with the difficulties of the planetary model and the need to revise it. Note that this section presents a historical development of the atomic model and illustrates a nonlinear path of science. Students can work on end-of-chapter problems 2–4 in recitations or lectures.

II. Bohr's Model of the Atom

The next step in the investigation of the atomic structure is Bohr's model. Although its applicability is very narrow and it does not represent any ideological shift from classical physics, we have included the model with all of its mathematical complexity in this book. The main reason is that it allows students to create a concrete image of the atom and thus provides the link between the planetary model and the quantum mechanics model of the atom that students learn later. Tell the students about Bohr's postulates and then ask them to reason through ALG activities 27.1.7, 27.3.1, and 27.3.3 to get a qualitative feel for the usefulness of the model. The derivation of Bohr radii and one-electron atom energy states takes considerable time in lectures (ALG activity 27.3.3). Ask students to write down the fundamental equations used in the derivations (Coulomb force equation, Newton's second law for circular motion, the electrical and kinetic energies of the atom, and the postulate about quantized angular momentum). Show the results of the derivations, which are done in the book, using circular orbits of relative size and an energy state diagram. Ask the students to confirm that the Balmer spectral lines are consistent with atomic transitions from higher states to the $n = 2$ state—this is, in a way, a testing experiment (ALG activities 27.3.2–27.3.5).

Questions and problems that you can use with students in lectures and recitations to help develop student qualitative and quantitative understanding include ALG activities 27.2.3, 27.3.6—27.3.8, and end-of-chapter questions 3 and 4 and problems 8, 9, 20, 64, and 66. Notice that we do not talk about the electrons in excited states but atoms in excited states. This wording is chosen to reflect the fact that we treat the atom as a system, and it is the system (not the electron by itself) that has a certain amount of energy due to its configuration.

III. Spectral Analysis and Lasers

We spend considerable time on spectral analysis because it is one of the most important applications of the concepts in this chapter. Start students working on ALG activities 27.3.7, 27.3.8, and 27.3.9 or follow the textbook exploration in Section 27.3. There we discuss different ways that atoms are excited (thermal excitation), discharge tubes, and hot atoms (like on the Sun) colliding. Students investigate stellar spectra in Observational Experiment Table 27.2. Students often think that the dark lines in the stellar spectra are due to missing elements that do not emit light of particular wavelengths; thus, it is important that they test these ideas (Testing Experiment Table 27.3). Section 27.4 is dedicated to stimulated emission and methods to produce population inversion and laser light. End-of-chapter problems 14, 22, 27, and 28 can be used with students in lectures. ALG Section 4 with activities 27.4.1–27.4.10 provides a variety of problems that can be done in recitations and homework. ALG activity 27.4.12 is a great lab experiment (you can replace CO with any gas that you have available for the students to investigate).

IV. Quantum Nature of Atoms, the Exclusion Principle, and Many-Electron Atoms

Textbook Section 27.5 describes experiments and reasoning processes that led to the invention of the quantum numbers l, m_l, and m_s for electron states in multielectrons. The end of the section is dedicated to the summary of the quantum numbers along with the Pauli exclusion principle. Notice how this section describes historical struggles along this path and is a perfect example of how models that would later be proven to be wrong stimulate the scientific progress. Although this section contains rather complex material, we hope that the story it is telling will be compelling for the students. Question 12 could be used as a free-response question in the lecture.

Textbook Section 27.6 introduces students to a new concept of the wave nature of particles. The ALG sequence that parallels the textbook story is in activities 27.1.8–27.1.9, 27.2.4, 27.3.10, and 27.3.11. You can use these in lectures for discussions or in problem-solving recitations. The textbook uses a similar experimental and reasoning progression as that outlined in the ALG activities and also describes testing experiments for the concept of an electron as a wave (Table 27.4) and the story of Davisson and Germer. Although the textbook introduces the students to wave functions, we do it only qualitatively and suggest that you do not put this material on tests. Textbook Section 27.7 combines earlier results in the chapter to describe electron states in multielectron atoms and to analyze the periodic table. Students learn about the concept of subshells, shells, and ground state configurations. The ideas in these three sections (27.5–27.7) can be applied with students in lectures or in recitations to end-of-chapter problems 39, 40, 41, 43, 44, 46, 47, and 49.

V. The Uncertainty Principle

Textbook Section 27.8 develops the position-momentum version of the uncertainty principle (through the analysis of particle diffraction through a single slit) and then proceeds to the energy-time version. We use this later idea to explain electron tunneling and the possibility of mutations occurring in DNA replication. This happens if a proton in one of the strands that forms a bond between the electron pair on the opposite sides of the DNA spiral happens to be in the wrong well when the replication occurs. Students can apply the uncertainty principle in lectures or in recitations to end-of-chapter problems 55–58.

28

Nuclear Physics

Chapter 27 involved atomic models and atomic applications, including spectroscopy. In this chapter, students learn the composition of a nucleus. We follow the historical path here and continue to use the tools that students have developed, such as energy bar charts. The history is especially important in this chapter, not only because it provides an excellent example of how physicists construct knowledge but also because in this chapter students meet female physicists for the first time. So far, all the historical figures noted have been males.

The chapter is broken into four parts:

I. *Early nuclear models*
II. *Nuclear force, binding energy, and nuclear reactions*
III. *Radioactive decay, half-lives, and radioactive dating*
IV. *Ionizing radiation and its effects*

For each part, we provide examples of activities that can be used in the classroom and brief discussions of anticipated student difficulties with the subject matter.

Chapter subject matter	**Related textbook section**	**ALG activities**	**End-of-chapter questions and problems**
Early nuclear models	28.1, 28.2	28.1.2–28.1.5, 28.1.8, 28.1.9	Questions 1, 2, 6 Problems 1, 3, 5
Nuclear force, binding energy, and nuclear reactions	28.3–28.5	28.1.11, 28.3.2, 28.3.3, 28.3.5, 28.3.6	Problems 6, 10, 12–16, 18, 20, 24, 26, 60, 63, 64

Radioactive decay, half-lives, and radioactive dating	28.6–28.8	28.1.7, 28.3.1, 28.4	Questions 5, 7–9 Problems 28, 32, 38, 39, 42, 46, 48, 50
Ionizing radiation and its effects	28.9		Question 10 Problems 54, 56

I. Early Nuclear Models

Section 28.1 tells a story of the early development of understanding of the constituents of nuclei (the studies of radioactivity), focusing on the experiments that led to the concept of a changing nucleus. It starts with Becquerel's accidental discovery that uranium salt placed on top of a covered photographic plate exposed the plate. Marie and Pierre Curie studied the nature of the radiation sources exposing the photographic plates (Observational Experiment Table 28.1). Rutherford and his group deflected the radiation in a magnetic field (Testing Experiment Table 28.2) and found that the radiation consisted of alpha particles, electrons, and gamma rays. This discovery ultimately led to a nuclear model whose constituents were alpha particles and electrons.

ALG activities 28.1.2–28.1.5 provide a sequence of exercises for the students to do before or in parallel with reading the textbook. You can work though the ALG activities in class with them and then assign the textbook section for homework or let them read the textbook on their own and then do ALG activities. Note a short discussion of the process that led to the discovery of the proton by Rutherford and colleagues at the end of textbook Section 28.1.

The experiments described in Section 28.1 led physicists to believe that there were three types of radiation emitted by atomic nuclei, one of which behaved as an electron and one as an alpha-particle. Therefore, it was reasonable to hypothesize that electrons and alpha particles were inside the nuclei. Textbook Section 28.2 explores the possibility that the electron was a nuclear constituent. We show with calculations, based on the uncertainty principle, that if that were the case, the positive kinetic energy of the electron should have been too large compared with the negative electric potential energy of the interaction of the electron with the nucleus, therefore making it impossible for the electron to be bound inside the nucleus. The calculation is rather complicated, so you will need to decide whether your students are ready. If you do decide it is too much, you can discuss in qualitatively.

To prompt students to start thinking about the issue, you could start with ALG activity 28.1.8 and then lead a whole-class discussion on the subject. Here it is productive to draw a bar chart for the nucleus as a system. Because the electrons cannot be in the nucleus (they were needed to explain the charge and the mass of the nuclei and especially alpha particles), then what gives the nucleus (and an alpha particle) its mass? A neutral particle was proposed as a nuclear constituent and was discovered at Cambridge in experiments by Chadwick (ALG activity 28.1.9). The new nuclear model now consisted of protons and neutrons. Neutrons explained the observations of isotopes for some nuclei (Observational Table 28.3). Notice the gradual building of the nuclear model, showing the process through which scientists continuously invent and refine models for the observed phenomena. It is another opportunity for students to get a clear picture of the process by which scientists build their knowledge.

We introduce the ${}_{Z}^{A}\mathrm{X}$ terminology for nuclei right after the neutron discussion. Students are fairly successful in acquiring the ideas in these two sections. To help develop facility with these ideas, they could work through Conceptual Exercises 28.1 and 28.2 in the textbook and then answer multiple-choice questions 1, 2, and 6 and then later in lectures and recitations work on end-of-chapter problems 1, 3, and 5.

II. Nuclear Force, Binding Energy, and Nuclear Reactions

Section 28.3 in the textbook provides a logical sequence of arguments that lead to the need of an attractive force that nucleons exert on each other inside the nucleus. Consequently, because of this attraction we can talk about the negative energy of interaction of nucleons.

We do not define this energy as binding energy—if we did, it would be negative and look unusual on the graphs. Therefore, we choose to define the binding energy of the nucleus as the magnitude of the energy that must be added to the nucleus to separate its constituents. For the students, we start with the binding energy of the atom, and based on similar reasoning we predict the mass defect of the nucleus. This reasoning is tested in Testing Experiment Table 28.4. We suggest that you have a whole-class discussion following the logic of the section, building up to Table 28.4, with which students can work together in class repeating the calculations to make sure they understand what mass defect means. Students can work on ALG activities 28.3.2 and 28.3.2, which connect the mass defect and binding energy to the idea of fusion.

The goal of textbook Section 28.4 is to lead students to the rules governing nuclear reactions (Observational Experiment Table 28.5 or ALG activity 28.1.11 present reactions that have been observed and the reactions that have not been observed). Students analyze the data and deduce two rules that apply to all reactions: the electric charge is the same before and after the reaction (charge conservation (Z)), and the number of nucleons in the nucleus or mass number are the same before and after the reaction (conservation (A)).

The discussion that follows the invention of the two rules leads students to the idea that the energy should also be a conserved quantity in these reactions. Textbook Testing Experiment Table 28.6 provides students with the testing experiments for this rule. We do not describe the actual experiments in which the data could have been collected, just the outcomes, so this particular table is in a way a check-mark for the process through which the knowledge is constructed, rather than the description of a real experiment.

There is a very important consequence of the rules that students devise. If the products of the reaction have less mass than the reactants, the energy equivalent of the mass difference is provided to the reactants as kinetic energy. Thus, nuclear reactions can produce kinetic energy, such as the thermal energy on the Sun due to fusion reactions and in nuclear power plants due to fission reactions (ALG activities 28.3.2 and 28.3.3 and Section 28.5).

Notice the discussion about fusion in Section 28.5 and the worked example related to the energy of the Sun (Section 28.4). In Chapter 12, students did a calculation showing that the thermal energy of the Sun is not sufficient to maintain its luminosity for billions of year. Now they are exploring whether nuclear energy is a possible source. The fission receives a great deal of attention too. We first present an example of how breaking of large nuclei can produce energy (the example of the actual historical experiment) and then describe the history of the discovery of fusion, demonstrating once again the path that science takes from an unexpected result of an experiment to the creation of a new model and its subsequent testing.

The history of fission is important not only because it shows how scientists develop new models but also because one of the leaders in this process was Lise Meitner. So far students have met only two women that contributed to the development of physics—Marie Curie and her daughter Irène Joliot Curie. Lise Meitner is the third. We suggest that you spend time on the fission story to emphasize the importance of diversity in science. ALG activities that you can use to help students figure out the fission process on their own before they read the textbook are activities 28.3.5 and 28.3.6.

Students seem fairly successful in developing the ideas in these three sections. Problems that can be used with students in lectures and recitations to help develop student qualitative and quantitative understanding include problems 6, 10, 12–16, 18, 20, 24, 26, 60, 63, and 64.

III. Radioactive Decay, Half-Lives, and Radioactive Dating

Students learned about the three types of radioactive decay (alpha, beta, and gamma) in the first section of the textbook, but they did not have enough knowledge to explain the mechanism of those processes. Now that they are equipped with the knowledge of the constituents of the nucleus, they can dig into the mechanisms.

You can begin with ALG activity 28.1.7, which represents the work of Frederick Soddy, and then have a discussion of the mechanism behind the reactions following the reasoning (Section 28.6) or vice versa. Notice the logic that leads to the neutrino hypothesis and the weak interaction idea (another demonstration of the path of science)—when evidence cannot be explained using existing models, physicists invent new models and subsequently test them experimentally. We suggest that you lead students through the worked examples in this section so that they get a feel for the numbers involved in the processes, especially the energy that is released. Especially important is Example 28.9, which analyzes the energy absorbed in our bodies due to potassium-40 decay—an interesting biological example that provides a real-life connection for the students.

Students can develop the idea of the half-life of radioactive decay of a radioactive sample by working with ALG activity 28.3.1 and reading Observational Experiment Table 28.7. They are capable of developing a relatively simple rule $N/N_0 = 1/2^n$ for the ratio of radioactive nuclei remaining after n half-lives. Everything is fairly straightforward to this point, and many quantitative calculations can be done by the students using just these ideas. The math becomes more difficult when the decay rate ($\Delta N/\Delta t = -\lambda N$) and exponential function are introduced. The decay rate equation needs some careful attention (why the minus sign, the meaning of λ and its relationship to half-life, and why the decay rate is proportional to N).

In Section 28.8, we derive an expression for the age of a radioactive sample with its application to carbon dating. Unfortunately, there are a reasonable number of equations based on the exponential function and used in applications in Sections 28.7 and 28.8. We suggest that you make an effort after all of the equations have been derived to organize them and their applications into a neat table so the material does not become an equation searching plug-and-chug effort by the students. There are several interesting biological applications in these sections, including use of radioactive carbon nuclei to determine the source of carbon in plants, the volume of blood in the human body (Example 28.10), and determining the age of an old bone. All problems in ALG section 28.4, end-of-chapter questions 5, 7, 8, and 9, and problems 128, 32, 32, 38, 39, 42, 46, 48, and 50 provide good practice for the students in lectures, recitations, and homework.

IV. Ionizing Radiation and Its Effects

All of Section 28.9 is devoted to the definitions of quantities used to describe the absorption of ionizing radiation by the human body: absorbed dose (rad), biological effectiveness, and dose equivalent (rem). Conceptual Exercise 28.12 estimates the number of ions produced by a chest X-ray. We proceed to the discussion of the natural and human-made sources of ionizing radiation, along with the effects on the body of ionizing radiation. Students can apply the ideas in this section in lectures or in recitations by working though end-of-chapter question 10 and problems 54 and 56.

29

Particle Physics

Chapters 25, Relativity, and Chapter 28, Nuclear Physics, form the basis for some of the material in this chapter. We examine the most recent developments in microscopic physics (particle physics) and in the cosmological history of the universe. The chapter is broken into three parts:

I. *Particle physics*
II. *Fundamental interactions and the standard model*
III. *Cosmology*

For some parts, we provide examples of activities that can be used in the classroom to help develop the ideas. We do not treat the material in this chapter, especially toward the end, quantitatively. It is under development at the forefront of present physics research.

Chapter subject matter	**Related textbook section**	**ALG activities**	**End-of-chapter questions and problems**
Particle physics	29.1	29.1.1–29.1.3, 29.2.1–29.2.4	Problems 3–9, 41
Fundamental interactions and the standard model	29.2, 29.3	29.2.5–29.2.8, 29.3.1, 29.3.2	Questions 1–4 Problem 42
Cosmology	29.4, 29.5	29.1.5–29.1.9, 29.2.9, 29.2.10, 29.4.3	Problems 34, 36

I. Particle Physics

The focus in Section 29.1 is on the early proposal of the existence of anti-particles, on the discovery of these particles, and on the interesting applications of anti-particles in our lives. On the basis of his theory of relativistic quantum mechanics, Paul Dirac first predicted the existence of virtual electrons in negative energy states, which then became positive holes (positive electrons) when in excited positive states. Carl Anderson detected positive anti-electrons called positrons in 1931 (see Figure 29.1). Positrons could be produced by the radioactive decay of medium light nuclei, such as ^{11}C, ^{13}N, ^{15}O, ^{22}Na, ^{40}K; by pair production due to a high-energy gamma ray; and by the transformation of a proton into a neutron in a nucleus. The annihilation of positrons by pair annihilation is analyzed in Conceptual Exercise 29.1(see Figure 29.2). Positron emission tomography (PET) is analyzed at the end of Section 29.1 and in Figure 29.4. Other anti-particles are introduced at the end of the section. Students can work on Active Learning Guide (ALG) activities 29.1.1–29.1.3 and 29.2.1–29.2.4 and textbook end-of-chapter problems 3–9 and 41.

II. Fundamental Interactions and the Standard Model

After a brief introduction to the four fundamental interactions, students focus on the electromagnetic interaction. We compare action-at-a-distance model to the field interaction, which is mediated by the exchange of a virtual photon. Because the interaction can be over a long distance and involve a relatively long time interval Δt to occur, according to the uncertainty principle the energy of interaction $\Delta E \geq \hbar/\Delta t$ is small. We then introduce the other interactions with their particle mediators. The size in terms of the energy of these other mediators depends on the distance and time interval for the interaction. See the summary in Table 29.1. We summarize the units used in particle physics in Quantitative Exercise 29.2. Students can work on ALG activities 29.2.5–29.2.6, 29.3.1, and 29.3.2 and end-of-chapter questions 3 and 4.

The classification of elementary particles in terms of leptons such as electrons (Table 29.2) and hadrons such as protons and neutrons is the subject of Section 29.3. The hadrons (Table 29.3) are further broken into those with two quarks (mesons such as pions) and those with three quarks (protons, neutrons, and so on). We describe experimental support for the idea of hadrons being comprised of quarks (i.e., the experiments in which electrons are scattered from the hadrons) similar to the alpha particle scattering from protons and neutrons in gold nuclei. We follow with the review of the development and summary of the standard model near the end of Section 29.3. Students can work on ALG activities 29.2.7 and 29.2.8 and end-of-chapter questions 1 and 2 or problem 42.

III. Cosmology

A 13.7 billion history of the universe since the big bang is provided in Section 29.4. Students should know that their bodies are composite objects constructed from particles that have been around for 13.7 billion years; the heavy elements such as carbon, iron, potassium, and so forth were produced during supernova events and made their way to Earth over that time interval.

The recent unsolved mysteries involving dark matter and dark energy are the subjects of Section 29.5. Students can easily understand the need for dark matter by using circular motion dynamics to analyze the speed of our own Earth about the galactic center. This can be extended to the motion of galaxies in the Coma Cluster. The source of the missing mass that is needed to cause the higher speed circulation is an unsolved problem. An even greater problem is the source of dark energy that is causing the universe to expand at an accelerating rate. Together the dark matter and dark energy must amount to about 94 percent of the mass energy in the universe. There are many problems in physics left to understand. The pursuit of this knowledge is the subject of the brief concluding Section 29.6 of the textbook. Problems that students in lectures and recitations can work to help appreciate the need for dark matter and dark energy are ALG activities 29.1.5–21.1.9, 29.2.9, 29.2.10, and 29.4.3 and end-of-chapter problems 34 and 36.

II. Cosmology